Coppi's Angel

Coppi's Angel

UGO RICCARELLI

TRANSLATED BY MICHAEL McDERMOTT

L'Angelo di Coppi
© 2001 Arnoldo Mondadori Editore SpA, Milano

**Middlesex
University
PRESS**

First published in 2007 by Middlesex University Press

Translated from:
L'Angelo di Coppi
© 2001 Arnoldo Mondadori Editore SpA, Milano

Translation and footnotes © Michael McDermott

ISBN: 978 1 904750 24 6

A CIP catalogue record for this book is available from
The British Library

Design by Helen Taylor

Printed in the UK by Cambridge Printing

Photographs of Coppi, Torino, Garrincha, Johnson, Zatopek and the Kiev memorial to FC Start, reproduced courtesy of PA Photos

Photographs of Nuvolari, Whymper and Pasolini, reproduced courtesy of Getty Images

Middlesex University Press
North London Business Park
Oakleigh Road South
London N11 1QS

Tel: +44 (0)20 8411 4162
Fax: +44 (0)20 8411 4167

www.mupress.co.uk

Cover image: Torino football team 1948, reproduced courtesy of PA Photos

Winners are unaware of what they are losing.

GESUALDO BUFALINO

*To Fausto Guccinelli, who pedalled with me
for many years*

TRANSLATOR'S NOTE

Ugo Riccarelli's stories in this collection are linked by nostalgia for a time before sport had become a global marketing enterprise. Sport here is a source of aesthetic thrills, heightened by moments of inspiration in which the participants reveal part of their souls. Each chapter recalls the artistry and style of characters who have taken on symbolic roles in the history of their sports.

Riccarelli approaches well-known figures from fresh and unusual perspectives. He freely mixes real and imagined events, sometimes involving the characters' dreams where their insecurities and worries are laid bare. Riccarelli is interested in showing the vulnerability in people well known for their talents.

Darker forces are at play in these stories, with the spectre of untimely death hovering over gifted characters. The presence of death adds an evanescence to the feats being described and seals a legendary status for men whose lives were ended prematurely.

In Riccarelli's stories sport is seen as a method of communication between people who meet each other unexpectedly. Sport is a release from the mundane and troublesome business of daily living. While the sporting events are unfolding, the routines of life are suspended, bringing joy to those privileged to be watching, and alleviating some of their suffering.

The powerful Italian prose of these stories is created with an economy of words, and rich imagery is constructed through clear, precise descriptions. In translating from Italian I have tried to maintain the sense of the original text as much as possible. At times Riccarelli uses slang, or vocabulary specific to a sporting situation, which has been transferred into as near an equivalent as possible in English.

The gentle humanity of these stories is too easily lost in the frenzied world of modern sport. Riccarelli reminds us of the simple yet profound influence that sport can have on the human condition, an influence far deeper than the commercial mire in which modern sport often flounders.

M.M.

CONTENTS

Coppi's Angel

On 12 February 1959 Fausto Coppi came out of the gate to his villa. He stopped for a moment to look at the mist between the Castellania hills, and he thought of the sun he had seen in Spain. It had comforted him like an old friend, it had warmed his back and for a while it had eased his fatigue. The wheels of the group in front had quickly gone on ahead, and he often looked down at the tarmac slipping past as he pretended to be his former self, smiling weakly at the people who lined the side of the road. Above him the sky was blue and the sun shone down on his back. A breath of wind brought cheerful shouts of encouragement and snatches of conversation. Inside him was a cold feeling, the faraway burden of something that disturbed him but he could not understand exactly why. At Sueca he had been distracted by a bird that had flown up lazily from a field. It looked like a pheasant and for a moment he had followed it with his gaze, as if he had a shotgun in his hands rather than handlebars. He did not see the hole in the road, which threw him onto the ground with a sharp bump. Two fingers broke without his feeling a thing. When he could stop and lift himself up he did not call out in complaint. Instead he looked at the thing that was watching him from the top of a tree, which he thought must be the pheasant.

Coppi left his home slowly and entered the mist. He was due to cycle towards Acqui and then through the climbs and descents of the road as far as Ceva. He had three days of rest at Mongelli's house, to find his good legs before the meeting in France. Three days of freedom with his old friend before the circus of bike wheels, planes, massages, journalists, the French and everything else would start up again.

Near Roccaverano the sun broke through the cloud and calmly

accompanied him as he effortlessly turned the pedals. Coppi talked to himself as he pedalled. He thought of his future that was now as strung out as the group escaping into the distance. He would have to gain time and reach them before the gap increased. He looked around for a teammate, but there was no one to give him a hand, to help him back to the group with the minimum of effort. There was no one to make a pact with, to promise some easy money, to do him a favour, as in a minor race. The sun tried to shake off the mist as the group edged further away; the multi-coloured backs of the cyclists disappeared into the fog and were swallowed up along with the road. It was too cold, and they were too far away, Coppi thought; he couldn't make up the distance. So he began to think of what he could possibly do now, as he had done many times before, of what tactics to use. Perhaps he should stop pedalling and wait for the team car. He could retire claiming liver trouble, or an upset stomach, or a pain in his hand. Coppi imagined a light touch on his shoulders, a soft push on the saddle. Ettore Milano would give him a bit more petrol in the tank. He'd only need him for a couple of hundred metres and then he'd reach the group. He remembered Magni and Bartali. A glance at Martini's bald head. Perhaps he could also see Baldini. 'Go on Ercole, see you back at the hotel.' He looked up and saw his future getting further away, escaping from him at the end of the road and he felt as though he was falling asleep.

After Cortemilia the fog had turned thick and Coppi continued in thought as he pedalled. The cold bit through his calves and his soaking leggings, stinging the bone like a woodpecker hammering at the trunk of a fir tree. The road rose up, and in the mist he could hear only the sound of the tyres on the tarmac and the turn of the pedals.

'I'll keep pedalling,' Coppi said to himself, 'I'll push a bit harder and use the forty-eight gear ratio.' He changed gear, hearing the noise of the chain in the almost total silence of the road.

Suddenly to his side he noticed that the sound of the tyres had doubled. 'Fuuuuum, fuuuum,' he could hear a distinct rhythm. The first thing he saw was someone's back. It looked like a boy's back and a blonde head of hair. Then he saw the bike and he felt happy because it was a black Aquila, just like the first one he ever rode, with the low handlebars, large wheels, fixed gear and worn-off paint.

In a flash, the natural instinct of the champion was shaken. The wound of seeing himself overtaken made Coppi the competitor feel something harden inside his muscles. His pride had been pierced so he redoubled his effort and launched a counterattack.

He stood up on his pedals for a powerful burst, only to think how stupid and childish he must be. 'That I,' he said to himself, 'am now using my energy to chase down young lads! Are Giros, Tours, Stelvios not enough? I've climbed the Tourmalet, Aubisque and Croix de Fer, so why can't I let someone cycle in front of me without feeling the need to overtake him?'

He sat down straightaway and raised his hand in apology. 'Go on son, you've not even noticed that this chap bundled up in his leggings is the *Campionissimo*, the all time legend, the only man to command all the European roads on which he has raced.'

Coppi stayed a moment with these thoughts as he cycled. Again he clearly saw that back and that blonde hair that climbed with no visible effort, eating up the road and pedalling as easily as if he was on a touring holiday. The lightness of his pedalling strokes was so natural, his style so fluid, his rhythm so unhurried. Moreover the incline was steep and the Aquila was certainly no mountain goat, weighing at least fifteen kilos and moving like a geyser forced by the weight of the sand. And yet it climbed, with that fixed wheel and that fluid rhythm.

So it was natural for Coppi to push himself a bit harder, to see if he could catch the boy, telling himself that this must be a good way of tuning the legs, a good form of training without real competition. There was still about another kilometre to climb before they reached the tough Padre hill. 'With that incline he'll soon run out of steam,' thought Coppi. He changed his gear to a fifty and stood up to dance on the pedals, taking a few deep breaths to bring oxygen to those hidden areas of his calves. At the same time he could hear the huge pump of his heart pounding as he worked. Everything was as it always was, the Bianchi beneath him starting to hunt down the boy a few metres ahead, just as he had hunted down Bartali, Robic and Ferdi Kubler.

15

The boy turned at the first hairpin bend ten metres ahead of Coppi and two metres above him. As he changed gear, he gave the boy, now opposite him, a quick glance. He knew how to read races, to observe the pedalling of an opponent, to instantly understand the meaning of a smile or an open mouth, or the anguished grimace of exhaustion. Coppi knew how to appraise a breakaway and choose what to do.

Coppi didn't notice anything particular in the boy's style as he cycled on. He did not seem worried or tired, he didn't smile. He just carried on pedalling on that black Aquila, oblivious, as if he had been sculpted from stone.

At the second bend there were only five metres between them. As the boy turned, Coppi was just beneath him and he glanced again at his face. All he saw were two eyes fixed on the road, eyes that did not seem to notice that someone was nearby.

When the Champion turned he felt another stab in his chest. The boy, as though remembering something all of a sudden, stood up on his pedals and shot noiselessly away, leaving Fausto searching for the best gear for the last three-hundred metres of bends. Coppi reached the summit alone and saw no trace of the boy; but he smiled as he noticed the few beech leaves to survive such a bitter winter on top of the Padre. He had arrived with leaden calves, his head numbed; he felt foolish for having made such an effort when his legs were not fully ready. Without suitable preparation he had run the risk of breaking down, all because he could not bear to be overtaken. By the time he reached the final bend of the descent he had told himself to forget about the morning's events.

Mongelli and his wife were waiting in their garden to welcome Fausto. They went inside together and settled down in the warmth from the ceramic stove that had been imported from the Tirol. Coppi listened to their compliments, and he was pleased to think that tomorrow his friend Milano was coming, a day earlier than planned, bringing with him the faithful Cavanna[1] who carried such wisdom

1 Biagio Cavanna was Coppi's coach, masseur and confidante. He helped Coppi from the very start of his career.

in his hands. He spoke to his friends about his journey, but made no mention of his secret challenge with the boy; he said nothing because he'd already forgotten about it; surely he was mistaken about what had happened. Coppi settled himself into the room where Mongelli had left his luggage that was brought from the station, and he ran a hot bath. The room was full of steam like a Turkish bath. The bath was scented and hot, and Coppi immersed himself in the bubbles as, earlier, he had been immersed in the fog. He let his thoughts drift and was almost asleep when he shook himself with a start. Inside his drowsy head he could hear the noise of those tyres on the Aquila, 'Fuuuum, fuuuuum.' Although he was still submerged in the bathwater he noticed that his legs had begun to pedal again.

Next morning Coppi rose early and ate a large breakfast. He checked his tyre pressure and turned the chain to fine tune the gear change on his bike. He said goodbye to Mongelli telling him he would cycle for a couple of hours on the road (including a couple of sprints) to train his legs for climbing. He would take the route known as the big tour, sixty kilometres of ups and downs with the climb of the Padre at the end, a climb guaranteed to strengthen your lungs. As Coppi was about to leave, Mongelli put a hand on his shoulder, a small gesture to wish him the best of luck for the journey ahead.

The same road went by under the wheels, the same tarmac which coursed in Coppi's blood. His gearing system was new and lightweight, his derailleur the latest design that changed so smoothly. Coppi did not follow the group, but cycled calmly on his own. The weather was fine and he could see no ghosts in the mist.

Coppi reached the start of the Padre from the fork in the road where he had been passed the day before, but today he came from the right-hand side, a couple of hundred metres from the exact spot where he had been overtaken. The short climb was difficult for cars too, so the road was empty as motorists preferred to take an easier route. Coppi was enjoying the peaceful training ride; he had pushed himself a few times and his legs had responded without too much effort. He was going much better than the previous day when his inadequate preparation, combined with the humidity, had left him short of breath on the final climb. He remembered that lad who disappeared in the twinkling of an eye.

As if the thought of the boy had somehow made him appear, Coppi found him at his side three-hundred metres above the point where he had first appeared. He was riding the same Aquila with the same determination and that same smooth style. No sooner had Coppi realised who it was, than the boy had moved ten metres ahead.

'OK son, twice seems a bit too much,' Coppi thought to himself, as he changed down to the forty-nine–sixteen ratio in order to fight back. After a hundred metres he'd built up speed when the boy, who was coming to the bends, got up on the pedals and jumped away. 'Dirty swine, so you really want to race,' said Coppi to himself gritting his teeth. He remembered the brutal peaks he had scaled: the Galibier, l'Isere, the Gavia and many others. In comparison with his battles against Bartali, Kubler and Robic – the freezing mountains where bears roamed – the Padre was a walk in the park. Yet that madman was still there, sometimes six, or three, now seven metres ahead of him. Coppi belted along the road that seemed to be chafing the wheels of the heavy Aquila, and he reached the boy's back, searching for signs that he was puffing hard, only to find him in full sail as though blown by the wind. He was gliding along without a breath, like a marble sculpture on the surface of a lake.

It is this which most hurts the true cyclist. To see the back of your adversary; to see him move easily, with no signs of fear or of an imminent crack; to see him have no concern about the rival following his wheel, waiting for the moment to attack. They steadily rode the five tough bends before the Padre, and arrived at the summit one in front of the other. One was just a blonde lad, who rode like a butterfly on his worn, old, black Aquila. The other was Fausto Angelo Coppi, with a lung capacity of seven litres, riding a light, sleek Bianchi. In his head he carried memories of the millions of kilometres he had ridden; in his bones he felt pain and fatigue; he could remember the kisses of women he'd loved and of those he would never know; he heard the roar of the crowd and the flash from photographers; the attention of newspapers and journalists; heaps of victories and heaps of money; the adoration of the masses; and the mixture of respect and hatred for those who win too much. Fausto Angelo Coppi arrived at the top of the Padre in second place. He hurled himself into the descent as though throwing himself into a memory of the broad bends of the Stelvio where he had smashed Koblet, brushing the snow and stones as far as Bormio that had appeared from around a bend like an oasis in a mirage.

Descending the Padre was a real plunge, with ten wide curves where you could keep pedalling. Coppi was thinking about this as he saw the boy stand up on his pedals and pick up his pace. 'Bloody hell, what does he think he's doing?' But as he wondered at the boy's recklessness, he realised he had misjudged the bend, which turned more sharply than he remembered causing him to brake and swerve out into the small space he could find in the road.

Cycle racing meant that the roads were closed to cars. On training runs, cars could be met unexpectedly. So for Orlando Merighi, in his dazzling white Fiat Millecento with the blue roof, he only just had time to say to himself 'That looked like Coppi,' before he slammed on the brakes and yanked the steering wheel, making one of his white-rimmed wheels graze the edge of the ditch, while the Bianchi wobbled on. Fausto had only brushed the side of the car, so he quickly regained his rhythm as a worried Merighi jumped out of his car. But for Coppi the problems were just about to start.

'Where is he?' Coppi yelled to himself, his legs now turned to jelly after the scare. Following the frightening adrenalin rush, his strength was leaking away drop by drop. The weather was calm as he arrived at the long flat straight, and the still of the surrounding countryside seemed to be mocking him. 'That bastard's disappeared, there's no sign of him,' thought Coppi.

He cycled slowly towards Mongelli's house, thinking of many things, strange painful things for a great champion. 'I'm finished. I felt pretty strong, my lungs felt good, the bike was well tuned, but that lad is made of something special. That lad was riding a rusty bit of metal twice as heavy as my bike, he had no gears and yet he flew like the wind. He made my legs burn on the climb, and on the descent he disappeared in a flash.' Coppi was thinking these thoughts as he pedalled, thoughts which went to his very core, but when he saw Mongelli at his door everything seemed to return to normal. The house, his friend, the fresh air and that familiar smell of sweat after a hard ride were as they always were. Everything here seemed so real, that the boy resembled an image from a distant dream.

Sitting in an armchair after lunch as Mongelli's wife knitted, Coppi sipped a small cup of sweet coffee. As nonchalantly as he could, he asked his old friend what he knew of the young cyclists in the area. 'There's no one to speak of really Fausto. There's one good amateur, but he's no future champion. There's a kid called Remo Gilardi from Mondovi who's coming up. He's only eighteen, good on the flat and in time trials but he quickly starts to tread water on tough climbs and he often abandons the stage. No he's not blonde in fact he's dark haired. I can't think of anyone else with good legs. I'm sure there's nobody else. There's no one anywhere near to your class around here, I doubt anyone would be up to carrying your water bottles for you.'

That evening Coppi's mentor Cavanna arrived. Biagio Cavanna, the blind man with the magical hands. The two men held great affection for each other, and neither mentioned the intrigues surrounding the white lady, *la signora Giulia*[2]. Ettore Milano was there as well, and together they spoke of the future, of the prospects for tomorrow, and the following trip to France for the Six Day Race.

Coppi went with Cavanna to his room for a massage after the day's training ride. The blind man asked Coppi to stretch out on the bed so that his hands could listen to the messages sent from his aching muscles. He could tell the champion wanted to talk, about himself and other things, so he looked ahead into the darkness letting his hands work their magic on Coppi's calves.

'Biagio, please tell me if I still have my old strength,' asked Coppi.

2 Coppi, a married man, had caused huge public controversy by his affair with Giulia Locatelli, the wife of a doctor. He was eventually to leave his wife Bruna, and start a new life with Giulia.

'You still have enough power in your legs Fausto, but there's something that is troubling your mind,' replied Cavanna.

'I saw my old black Aquila being ridden by a demon, a blonde devil who has really disturbed me. I've wondered if I just dreamt it, because I can't seem to remember his face. On the slopes of the Padre I tried to overtake him – twice in fact, but he shot off like the wind each time.'

Cavanna gave him a knowing smile, the smile of a man who can understand a situation immediately.

'Remember that devils are fallen angels,' he said to Coppi, 'they travel the world restlessly without finding peace. It's plain that this one you're talking about is afraid of returning to where he has come from. He is not trying to race, but to escape. You have battled against other fiercer devils such as Louison Bobet, Koblet, Glass Head[3], even Van Steenbergen, do you remember? That damned Tuscan Gino or Ferdi Kubler who you caught before he had time to say amen. Remember when you broke Archimbaud's hour record burning away all the others in your wake. Don't worry about this lad, Fausto, he's got other things to worry about instead of racing. Let him go.'

Cavanna's hands were warm and they worked like fire inside his muscles. Quite suddenly Coppi fell asleep. He dreamt he was at a station waiting for a train. When the train arrived at the platform it did not stop and Coppi found he was chasing it for the rest of the night. The train stayed two or three metres ahead of him, and instead of the noise of the metal wheels on the rails he heard that 'fuuuum fuuuum.' of the rubber tyres brushing the road. Restlessly he followed this train throughout the night.

In the morning he went out to ride the same route, but after his conversation with Cavanna he felt more at ease. He now knew who he was waiting for. 'Let's see who you are, let's see what you're really made of, you won't drop me today. I'll keep my eye on you this time, I won't give up,' he thought. Inside himself Coppi felt a great strength

3 'Glass Head' was a nickname for the French rider Jean Robic. He earned the name because he wore a helmet after a crash in the Paris-Roubaix race which had fractured his skull. A fierce adversary of Fausto Coppi, he won the Tour de France in 1947.

21

and with this extra confidence he made his way to his appointment. As ever, the fork in the road was deserted, and as ever he took to the road listening and waiting.

Fausto Coppi had puzzling dreams. Sometimes he dreamt of snow-covered mountains in May, mountains he would have to climb, or sometimes he dreamt of faces screaming and twisted on a descent, eyes watering with the cold and exhaustion. His dreams could be of the Stelvio which leaves you short of breath, where even moving slowly is a kind of torture. He would dream of a woman's smile, the beautiful girl holding the flowers on the victory podium. The dreams would start suddenly, as soon as his eyes shut and he let himself drift. His dreams were also of a blonde lad with a dark shirt on a heavy Aquila who suddenly turns up while you are thinking and then disappears. Dreams could be surreal like a bike on which you cannot actually pedal. Sometimes they were about a situation where you know there is nothing you can do. They could be all of these things or nothing at all.

Once more the boy was next to Coppi, and this time he would not let him go. They took each bend together on the way up the Padre, the boy leading with his strong rhythm and Coppi tucked in close behind.

'Today I'm going to get the better of you,' Coppi said to himself, 'or I'll stick tight to your wheel as I did that time with Robic, going over the Aubisque.' After the summit of the Padre he threw himself into the descent. Fearlessly the lad flew down. 'He's a real demon,' thought Coppi as he tried desperately to keep up. He followed him onto the flat, still at a high tempo and, where the road went up to the right towards Mongelli's house, the boy turned down to the left onto a small road that led to a large farm.

Coppi slowed the bike and watched the lad go into the farm. He plucked up his courage, dismounted the Bianchi and went to the door on foot. In the farmyard the boy too had dismounted, and was standing talking to an old woman at a door, who Coppi thought might be the boy's mother.

'I'll introduce myself and we'll see what happens,' said Coppi to himself. So he took off his cycling cap and dark glasses, as he would do when meeting important people, in preparation to offer a handshake and an introduction before requesting an explanation from the boy.

'How do you do signor Coppi, I've been waiting for you,' said the boy, leaving Fausto dumbfounded.

As Coppi stared at him trying to comprehend his own bewilderment, the boy went into the house, giving Fausto a nod inviting him to come inside.

Coppi mumbled an 'excuse me' to the woman as he went into the dark of the house. Outside the sun had been very bright, so Fausto looked for a moment, taking time to accustom his eyes to the gloom, taking in the room little by little until he could see in the dark. He saw a poor but dignified kitchen, like so many in the countryside. He noticed a large kitchen cupboard, the kind that everyone had in those parts, which reminded him of his mother. All the houses in the country have a large dresser and a cupboard made of cherry wood where the glass is kept. On another wall he saw photos of himself and several headlines cut from newspapers: 'Coppi wins the Giro', 'The King of the Stelvio', 'One man is in the lead', 'The Tour de France is ours.'

Then Coppi noticed an armchair, and on this chair was something he found hard to comprehend at first. Perhaps it was a man, perhaps it was something else. The being had a huge head with a large forehead; he was not wearing a hat. Coppi saw two watery eyes above a narrow mouth, two stumpy arms and almost no legs. With emotion, the boy's faint voice said: 'Look Felice, signor Coppi has come to see you.'

The being seated in the armchair slowly stretched out a hand to touch the champion as he came near. Coppi felt his gentle touch, the familiar warmth of admiration.

So it felt natural for Coppi in the silence and the shadows to take off his fine woollen cycling shirt and offer it as it was, worn, sweaty and slightly faded. Felice accepted it without a word, but Fausto just made out a slight groan as a kind of smile moved on the lips, his eyes still staring above Coppi's head. Fausto stood straight up, feeling self conscious with his chest bare, that feeble pigeon chest that would have been embarrassing to him if it had not been for his achievements on the bike. He made a movement to overcome his own unease, and the discomfort he felt for the being in the chair, who was watching him. Coppi slowly raised a hand in a kind of salute, and as he left the room he accepted the fresh cycling shirt that the blonde boy was holding out.

'Thank you, thank you for everything,' said the boy. 'Felice is a great fan of yours. He listens to all the reports on the radio and he's always wanting to read about you and your races. Felice has water on the brain, so he communicates with his eyes. When you win a race he is really happy, he listens to the radio with as much as attention as if you were with him in the house. He follows everything avidly, the mountain stages, the sprints, the long escapes, every move within a race.'

Coppi looked down embarrassed.

'Please,' he said, 'you don't have to thank me.'

Outside the countryside lay silent, and the conversation between the two men stopped for a moment. When Coppi saw the Aquila leaning against a wall he turned to the boy with a question.

'Why don't you race on your bike? You're as fast as a rocket.'

'I ride every day as far as the brickyard, then I climb the Padre in a hurry because my mother always needs me to help out with my brother.'

'No, what I meant to say was why don't you compete, because if you did you'd be a champion for sure,' said Coppi, no longer embarrassed.

The lad smiled widely and replied: 'No thank you signor Coppi. I'm already doing plenty. You're enough of a racer for all of us. You were born to win, I'm born for other things.'

Having spoken, the boy gave a nod to the champion and went back inside the house.

Everything was still and silent in the countryside. The only noise came from Coppi as he sat on his bike and started to pedal again.

The Six Day Race passed by in a blur of meetings and the winning of easy money. For six days Coppi plied his trade, turning that chain and pedalling constantly. But a thought started to nag at him, the thought that the boy really could become a champion. He thought of the sight of the boy's back as he climbed the Padre, of his nimble descent and pace on the flat. He would have to speak to him again and convince him that everything could be worked out so that he could race while his brother was taken care of. He would take him into his team and help him, he could see to it that he would become a great cyclist, well to do and well respected. The lad would become fulfilled personally and entertain the crowds as well.

Coppi was satisfied as he returned to Italy, convinced that the boy's future would be easier. He thought he could leave the legacy of his triumphs to the blonde boy and his brother. As soon as he returned to Castellania he persuaded Milano to go out on his motorbike to lead him for a training ride. He asked to prolong the route as far as the Mongelli's house, saying that he had a surprise which everyone would appreciate.

It was 14 March and Coppi was happy. He liked to watch his beautiful son Faustino growing up. He would soon have someone else to whom he could try to explain the anguish he sometimes felt. Such were his thoughts as he pedalled at a steady rhythm behind the *derny*,[4] which Ettore Milano drove at a good pace to make his legs and lungs work hard.

Reports today still talk about it, the time that Coppi went off the main road to Alessandria in search of someone who he said did not have a name. Throughout the strange story he had never found out the name of the boy. He was so determined to find out the lad's name that he failed to notice the tractor on the straight road at Spinetta Marengo. As it edged out of a farm track onto the main road, Ettore Milano on the *derny* saw the tractor well in advance and swung wide to avoid it, convinced that Coppi would be paying attention and follow him with his customary agility. Unfortunately Coppi was racking his brains to try and remember the lad's name, and he hit the tractor at full tilt, falling to the ground without a murmur.

Although he had no broken bones as a result of the crash, it had been a serious blow, and he spent several days recovering. Eventually

4 A derny is a motorbike used to pace cyclists, usually in track races.

he managed to put his mind at rest about the boy, and was able to return home.

It was much later in December when Coppi and Geminiani had finished discussing details about the trip to Africa where hunting and malaria lay in wait[5], that he phoned Mongelli for a chat. As he spoke to his old friend the boy's face unexpectedly reappeared in his mind's eye, for it had been lost in the haze surrounding his sudden crash with the tractor. Coppi knew he must try once more to reach the boy.

This time he travelled by car, over the Padre and down the descent, stopping at Felice's house. He knocked on the door but no one came to answer. He went round to the fields where a man was working in the earth with a hoe, and he asked if he had seen the blonde lad or the woman.

'They went less than a month ago,' he replied, 'the brickyard closed and they went to Australia to find their fortune like so many others. Here the land is hard to work, and it's tough to make a living.'

'What about the other brother?' asked Coppi, by now quite disturbed, 'The one who was ill.'

'Felice. Are you talking about Felice?' said the man shaking his head. 'He stayed here, he didn't move.'

'Where can I find him then, I just want to say hello,' Coppi asked kindly.

The old man moved a hand across his face as if trying to wipe away some of his tiredness from working on the land. Then he looked straight at Coppi, deep into his eyes for several seconds without saying a word. Finally he turned his head to his right towards a hill, and pointed a finger, motioning that Felice was over there.

'He's over by the oak tree,' said the man.

Coppi thanked the man, making a sign to Milano to wait for him. From the pathway he noticed that the tree was not far away. He went over the brow of the hill and saw the oak tree, behind which stood a wall with an iron gate in it. He pushed the gate and went into the small enclosure. It was a tiny village cemetery, not as big as courtyard,

5 Coppi died from malaria contracted on this trip.

containing some crosses and marble slabs with small sculptures on them, a place where peace and sorrow existed together.

Coppi looked around calmly and he immediately recognised his own shirt. The colourful racing shirt was tied around one of the marble slabs. Beneath the slab lay fresh earth which had recently been pressed down, with a few flowers resting on the top.

He lifted the edge of the shirt with his hand. There was no photo on the marble because it is not done to show some people's faces. Instead there was a carefully written engraving in gold which read:

HERE LIES
FELICE
ANGELO
THE CHAMPION

The Trajectory of Life

In the autumn of 1933 Jerome Blanchot met Enzo Ferrari at the motor racing circuit in Pescara. They shook hands and talked at some length about cars and drivers. This was the era of dusty roads, of imposing machines as robust as tanks. The engines seemed sculpted from dark blocks of steel, with huge horsepower, capable of making the most terrifying sound. It now seems incredible that these beasts sped through the air on those enormous wheels as hard as marble.

The *Scuderia Ferrari* had grown from modest beginnings, from little more than a garage in Viale Trento eTrieste, Modena, with just four red Alfa Romeos to challenge for racing glory. Ferrari himself had ceased to drive, concerned for his son Dino's future, a future that was to prove short lived; so he acquired the best drivers of the time, who had left the Alfa team when they stopped competing in races. The flair of the aces Nuvolari and Varzi attracted many people to the team, and they quickly came to adore that word written beneath the prancing horse on the car bonnets.

Perhaps Blanchot was influenced by memories of epic deeds on that afternoon in Pescara, as he spoke in the *Modenese* dialect of a driver who was still just a lad but, as he explained to Ferrari, 'He can have explosive feet, or he can glide through a race with the delicacy of an artist with a paint brush.' He said the lad was a fascinating blend, his father being a Frenchman who had lived in Algeria, and his mother being Spanish. From this breeding came a son who was at ease in Paris or Africa, as accustomed to Spanish ways as to the breath of Saharan winds. All he wanted said Blanchot, was the right opportunity, and that opportunity would start with a handshake.

Some weeks later, in Viale Trento, Ferrari found himself opposite a young man wearing a silk scarf and a soft leather jacket, who was holding a cigarette in his hand like an artist's pencil – a detail which Ferrari found rather ill mannered. The young man was very refined and proud at the same time, speaking with just the few words necessary for conversation between a skilled driver and the man offering him a car. Ferrari's words were measured, probably because he was honouring his handshake with Blanchot, an able man whom he held in high esteem. The young man's name was Guy Moll, at that time unknown, but he was to take one of Ferrari's Alfas to race at Monte Carlo on 2 April 1934.

The course was as demanding as it is today. In those days it was an undulating three kilometres and one hundred and eighty metres, like a roller coaster, and without the chicane which was designed later on. The drivers belted down the roads with the force of seven hundred and fifty kilos, the cars directed using giant steering wheels, without the electronic wizardry of today. The engineers relied on levers and hammers, drops of oil and grease to smear on the moving parts, and the drivers wore fighter pilot goggles over leather bonnets that rarely required repairing.

Guy the novice did not excite the crowds in the qualifying rounds, where there were established drivers ahead of him, wily old foxes. There was Count Trossi in another Ferrari who did well in practice, and Chiron, the enfant du pays. Varzi was already a legend and Dreyfus, in his Bugatti, lined up with Trossi on the front row of the grid. There were six Alfa Romeos, five Maseratis and four Bugattis about to race over one hundred laps for the sheer thrill of it. They flew along, shaving past houses, swallowing up the air, burning through time, with drivers manoeuvring the cars from their cockpits, hardly protected from ravaging wind or punishing fatigue.

Dreyfus took the lead, and built up a big gap ahead of Chiron who was chasing hard. From the pits, Ferrari started to keep a watchful eye on his new lad, who seemed a bit uncertain, and who had actually looked scared at the start. For Monte Carlo you need guts, and with those guts you need strength, because after about an hour's racing you lose the feeling in your hands and legs; everything else ceases to exist except the deafening noise and the wind. If you are just a lad, the speed can be exhilarating, so much so that you can push your car to the point of no return.

After the first few laps Ferrari noticed Guy seemed to have settled himself, the tone of the Alfa's engine was sweeter, like a deeply contented laugh. His car seemed to emerge out of a huge roar from the end of the long straight. As Ferrari moved out of his box to gain a better view, Moll tore down to the tight bend at the gasometer, and the smile was swiped off Ferrari's face as he saw his driver come into the bend like a lunatic. The crowd in the stands gasped with anxiety, expecting Moll to leave the road, they imagined a smash and explosion to follow. Ferrari too felt queasy, perhaps Moll had overdone it; he saw the little face squashed in the cockpit, the tone of the engine a fraction too high, with the absence of a jarring sound of brakes on wheels.

Instinctively Ferrari kept his eyes on Guy's face, which somehow seemed calm, with almost a smile as he bent into the curve of the road. Then he watched the car slide sideways, grazing a post on the inside of the bend, before straightening out ready to blast down the straight part of the course.

'That was like Nuvolari,' thought Ferrari, 'that amazing slide that only Tazio was capable of; that courage and recklessness, the signs of someone who shows from within the class of a real artist.' He turned back to his staff, certain that he had witnessed again the substance of a real champion, certain that he had understood how important this was.

René Dreyfus had been passed by Chiron who flew on towards a certain victory. As the race pushed on to a conclusion Louis Chiron, a Monaco local, saluted the cheering crowd behind the crash barriers, waving an imperious hand at Mirabeau and sending a kiss in the direction of the stands at St Devote.

Meanwhile, Guy Moll slid into the bends, dancing a kind of tango through the ups and downs of the course. Reports later said that Chiron was amazed when he realised that the crowd's movement was not in salute of him, but out of shock at that red thing that was almost on top of him, like a thunderclap.

Perhaps because of the pressure created by the threatening roar behind him, perhaps because of simple misfortune, Chiron now lost his grip on his champion's expertise. On the last lap, on the descent into Mirabeau where before he had waved to the crowd with such hubris, he caught a puddle of spilled oil and skidded into the sandbags on the edge of the track. Guy Moll arrived alone at the finishing line, and grinned to the mechanics and the crowds. Ferrari ran up to him, asking where the hell he had learnt to handle the bends with such artistry, to which Moll's cocky reply was in perfect keeping with someone fully aware of the rarity of his natural gifts.

'When I was a boy in Africa, *monsieur*, I used to drive camels you know.'

Some time later during the race at Montenero, the young man fixed forever a place in Ferrari's heart, while chilling the blood of many who watched his display.

He started very fast behind his team mate Varzi, following him into the outside of the bends, with the innate skill of one who had driven like this all his life. In a few laps he had built a distance between himself and the other drivers, including Achille Varzi. In the midst of this frenzy his tyre punctured, and he was forced to return to the pits for repair.

Ferrari himself was caught between enthusiasm for his new prodigy who performed these miracles, and concern for his other champion driver, who was as proud and touchy as any thoroughbred. He had wanted to speak to Moll, but he let the moment go, reasoning that he had already been hindered by back luck, and that a wise team manager would not interfere too much.

Ferrari had not accounted for the fury and desire which the boy showed as he shot out of the pits and, after a lap, was once again breathing down Varzi's neck, about to lock him battle again. Achille was a fierce competitor, who loathed being overtaken by anyone. Those who witnessed the two men drive that day would say they had witnessed something of great beauty. A master craftsman mocking another great driver, stealing his space, as he traced outrageous trajectories across the track, flawlessly entering and leaving corners without a trace of hesitation or nerves.

The team manager Ferrari made a tough decision. He said to himself that it was a mistake for team mates to risk life and limb in a duel between each other, there was no sense in it at all. It was clear what had to be done. He prepared a sign saying 'Slow down,' which told Guy that he must ease off the pressure.

With the sign in his hand Ferrari saw Varzi reach the bend at pace, with Moll close behind. Half way into the bend, as Varzi was beginning to straighten up, Guy's car started a kind of crazy waltz, swinging close to the barriers. Ferrari noticed that instead of Moll's body looking rigid with fear as the car spun, he passed in front of the box and, turning to his team manager, almost saluted him. Moll glimpsed the sign in Ferrari's hand, and with the car still dancing, gestured to his manager that he understood and had everything under control. Quite right, it was not worth taking unnecessary risks. He stopped the car from spinning with a deft twitch of the steering wheel and carried on calmly behind Varzi.

Ferrari stood by the pit wall, incredulous. Never before had he seen someone drive with such *sangfroid*, such calm and skill in the midst of such peril. Ferrari was sure of the class of this young man, he understood the potential he was showing, and yet he felt a shiver run down his spine that left him feeling cold. There was no place for danger in this man's psyche, and other drivers became mediocre in comparison to the genius he showed as he swung through the bends.

The shiver had given Ferrari a heavy heart, and as he went to greet Guy after the race he felt almost paternal towards his new driver. He certainly wanted to congratulate him on his performance, but he also wanted to explain the concern he had felt. The mechanics were joking cheerfully as they tidied up, and Guy lent languidly against a wall, with a cigarette held in his fingertips like an artist's pencil. Ferrari looked him directly in the eye and said, 'Good effort son, but be careful what you're doing, because around you turns an unforgiving, brutal world. You need to start thinking as you go into those bends, where you are going to end up, who you have next to you and who is watching you.'

Moll's eyes lazily looked at the grey smoke wafting upwards, and he made a vague gesture with his cigarette as he said:

'I move in trajectories *monsieur* Ferrari. I try to design in the way that I think is right. As soon as I make my design it disappears leaving no trace, like the smoke from my cigarette. I cannot do anything else, apart from driving with this style, inhaling as I take my course, then letting the smoke go free in the air, to go wherever it wants to go.'

A few weeks later in August, the circus gathered for the Pescara Grand Prix, and the Coppa Acerbo. Guy Moll was set to drive the Alfa towards Montesilvano, to once again design his trajectories on the track. But he would never know how he would have performed, whether he would have floated as free as the smoke in the air, he was not even able to follow the race from home. Ernst Henne had mumbled a few words, saying how he had been in his silver Mercedes ahead of Moll, and had heard the whine of the Alfa engine as it came to overtake and then spun around in a sort of haze. The Alfa smashed into the side of the track, and the young man's life was stopped there on the road, a strange kind destiny fulfilled.

Ferrari carried on his work as team manager. With Moll's death consigned to history, he watched other drivers come and go. Perhaps he was like a father to them, even if he had been described as running his team like a despot. His own son Dino had made the rational choice not to be a racing driver.

Dino had been ill and died young. He had suffered from a viral nephritis that kept him bedridden for months, with his father at his side searching for a rational explanation. He convinced himself that his son was like a car, his body a type of engine, which could be adjusted and revised as necessary. Ferrari had a notebook in which he itemised a schedule for his son's recovery, where he wrote details of the tests that had been carried out. The book contained graphs and diagrams and curved shapes like the plan for a racetrack.

The final entry in the notebook was on 30 June 1956. The last phrase read: 'The battle is lost,' and he closed the book as at the end of a race. Ferrari made a quick mental calculation: Dino was twenty-four years old, the same age as Guy Moll, he thought.

Maybe it was because of these thoughts, or because of the associated ideas buried deep in memory, which we don't see and don't want to see, that as he left the hospital bedroom he noticed Doctor Santoni leaning languidly against a wall, holding a cigarette in his fingertips as if it was an artist's pencil.

In the darkness of the hospital corridor, the dim light from a window caught the cigarette smoke as it rose. Ferrari noticed it dance as it rose, then spin and twirl, making twists in the air, turning again, escaping, making circles and zigzags, like the fragile trajectories of a life.

The Invincibles

There is nothing very remarkable about being immortal.

JL BORGES

On the afternoon of 4 May 1949, Don Ricca Tancredi went to his room on the first floor at the Superga Basilica. His skin seemed to be burning, and he had started to feel short of breath so he poured some water into the old enamel wash basin and washed his face and hands. Instead of staying inside the presbytery, he had spent the afternoon walking outdoors, so his face was a little sunburnt and windswept. With great care he dried himself, took a deep breath, and sat down on the bed putting the back of his hand on his forehead to gauge his temperature. His skin felt cool but the burning sensation remained. Don Tancredi stood up, walked to the window and looked out over the Piedmontese hills. The rain and fog seemed to be closing in on the Basilica.

As he looked out he thought of his mother. He could hear her voice resounding in the room, and for a moment he was sure that he felt the gentle touch of her hand. 'It would be good if I could fall ill,' he thought, 'to have a raging temperature so that I could hide under my duvet and wait for that gentle hand to comfort me, that soothing hand to bring back my strength.' Don Ricca thought of his mother checking his pulse, when she would bring the bed sheet above his head to hide him for a moment from the outside world. 'Then everything would be at peace again,' he thought, 'in the cool white light from the linen.' After a while, as if the spell was lifting, the walls of the room would start to take shape again and everything would return to normal, quiet and ordered.

Don Ricca dwelt on these distant memories for a few moments. Then he looked around the room, taking in the modest material possessions that had accompanied him through life as if he was seeing them for the first time. There was the small table carved from cherry wood that he used for writing, his kneeler on which he prayed, the enamel wash basin, the bed he was sitting on and, leaning against the wall near the door, stood his library, his treasured books on their shelves. These humble possessions seemed to wait for him here, silent and unchanging, day after day. Don Ricca thought of the outside world, of the war that had recently finished, of the promise of victory which had brought only misery, ruin and broken lives. Half the world had been devastated but his few possessions remained with him in the same place every day, waiting for the storm to blow over, and for this he was grateful.

He stood up and walked over to the cherry-wood writing desk which he wiped with the palm of his hand as if wiping away a thin film of dust, smiling appreciatively to himself as he stroked the carved wood. Standing opposite his bookshelves he touched the spine of each book with his index finger, stopping for a second as if called by a memory: Balzac, Stendhal, Bernanos, Petrarca, Leopardi, Manzoni... each name was like a handshake from an acquaintance, an old friend with whom he had shared happy times. As his memory slowly ran through the familiar stories, his breathlessness eased and the burning sensation started to leave his head. For a moment Don Ricca felt almost happy.

It was when he reached a volume of Borges that his disquiet returned. How had that book with the battered spine finished up between Cervantes and Lazarillo? It had a strange title: *The Invincibles*. Delicately he removed it from the shelf. The white cover was torn, with a few dark burn marks as if it had been caught by flames. Don Ricca could not remember reading anything by the author and he could not remember having exchanged the book with one of his fellow priests as he often did. Trying hard to work out where the book could have come from, he went to the writing desk, switched on his reading lamp, rested the book on the desk and began to turn the pages carefully. At the top of page 43, blackened by smoke, he could make out the title of a chapter, the first lines of which ran as follows:

'People who leaf through a newspaper in the morning either do so to forget, or they are looking for something to make casual conversation about after lunch, so it is no surprise that they forget what they have read or, if they do remember, it seems rather hazy like a dream. To me, a modest reporter, fell the job of writing a report about what happened that afternoon, which can only be called a story of death. Whoever reads my few lines in the future, must not consider it to be fantasy or a mistake, any more than our normal lives can be considered fantasy or a mistake.'

After reading this Don Ricca was tempted to shut the book and pass quickly to another, but this kind of story had always unsettled him. He could have done without any other worries, as he already had plenty of his own, beastly worries, the sense of which he could not understand.

'For goodness sake, death is death,' he thought, 'even in fiction it doesn't do to upset the natural order of things too much.' But something stopped him from returning the book to the shelf, for it is often the things which are most disturbing that, at the same time, hold an attraction. Don Ricca remained a few minutes in thought with the page open in front of him before he summoned up courage, lowered his eyes and carried on reading.

'For whoever needs to know, my name is Luvanor Cruz, I am a sports reporter for *El Gráfico* newspaper from Buenos Aires. Don't fool yourself into imagining that this is an easy job. To describe athletic feats is to recount epic deeds, rather like those of Ulysses or Ithacus. I love the infinite variety of the worlds of Shakespeare and Brahms, so I have spent my time writing about Schiaffino's sublime skill, which arouses the same aesthetic pleasure as reading literary verses or listening to a classical symphony. However, it is not necessary to be a great scholar to see in a pass from Di Stéfano the moving perfection of a hendecasyllable. According to Freybart, sporting competition is a profound element of life, something men often misunderstand as they continue to run after the ball without fully understanding why. Searching for men's obscure motivation now seems to be a futile exercise, so I am content to merely report what has happened.

That autumn day of '48 is fixed in my memory, when Alvaro Mendez knocked on my door.

"I want to show you what it really means to play football," he said beckoning me onto the street with his hand. He did not say another word to me as we went by car to the River Plate stadium.

That was the first day that Pepe Minella took over the reins of the team. He had leant on the club president to release Pedernera so that the young Di Stéfano could take his place. From high up in the stands between the radio commentators we saw Minella arrive and stand in the middle of the pitch like the conductor of an orchestra, as he directed his team to their positions. He told Moreno to play on the right, and he pointed to Labruna to go to the left; then he gestured to Di Stéfano to play centre forward. After this the coach clapped his hands and the match began. It was like watching a beautifully crafted clock following the passage of time, of the passage of our lives, for the players moved in perfect harmony with each other, running purposefully or sliding into a tackle on a cry from Moreno. Di Stéfano moved with the grace of a dancer and the leather ball was given life as it slid between the players' feet. The goals came one after another like the inevitable result of a scientific formula. Today on paper I can write that this vision of perfection must have affected me profoundly.

Sitting in the same stands some months later, I witnessed River Plate's victory that gave them the championship for that year. Alvaro Mendez and Benito Laprida animatedly discussed and dismantled theories about the invincibility of that team. Their dispute contained points such as the pace of Epsineda and the accuracy of Aleman's shot. Their discussion took unusual turns including a philosophical direction that I found irresistible. Laprida, who had a Swedish mother (a Svennson from Uppsala) cited a seventeenth-century Swedish theory from Lars Erfjord which stated that invincibility is a mathematical function similar to infinity. Mendez cited Salmi, speaking of David and the mysterious theories held by the Essenes.

It was with great determination the next day that I climbed the staircase at *El Gráfico* to ask the director Jorge Alvarez for permission to carry out a survey into the strongest football teams in the world. I would need to describe how the clubs were organised, to get to know the personalities of the players and to learn about their football strategy so that I could comprehensively explain the secret of their invincibility.

Since that day I have thought many times of the enthusiasm with which I unveiled my plan to Alvarez. I can now admit that I was hoping for a sage response from the depths of his experience, instead of his simply acquiescing with the impetuous dream of a young journalist. However Alvarez accepted my suggestion, thereby pushing me on to this journey towards disaster.

Mendez and I spoke at great length to settle the details of my report and about organising a trip to Europe.

"You will start in Turin, Italy," he said to me definitely, "where there is a powerful team, which has been unbeatable for the last few years."

He showed me a cutting from *Futbol Internacional*. The report stated that this team had won the last four championships and was unbeaten at home for over eighty matches.

"You will see, Luvanor," Mendez said to me as he shook my hand, "that the secret of invincibility is to be found in that team. Go and see what it is that they do."

As I went up the stairs to the plane I stopped for a moment to breathe in the Baires air. It was the second of April 1949. The sky was incredibly clear, with dazzling sunshine rebounding off the metal wings and blinding the eyes. I turned away to protect my eyes from the glare, and I read on the side of the cockpit that the plane was called *Icarus.*'

Don Ricca Tancredi felt as if he too might have been blinded by the sun, so he stopped reading and rubbed his eyes. The table lamp seemed to flash and its brightness remained imprinted on his retina, making a curious kaleidoscope of colour appear on the little table. In the centre of this light he thought he saw the word 'Icarus' hewn onto the cockpit of a plane surrounded by sunlight, a plane that was travelling towards Turin. How strange he thought, that of all the possible flight routes, there is a plane from Argentina on its way here. He looked out at the sky and smiled, but the sky above Turin that

41

day was leaden and covered in a thick fog.

Nevertheless they say that the skies above have nothing to do with the deeds of men, and that an invincible team is just eleven people who can make others dream, who can make them forget their cold and their fears.

As he continued reading, Don Ricca smiled to himself.

'Turin seemed to me an elegant lady who was managing to hide her missing teeth with great dignity. The war had destroyed many houses and several streets were still full of large holes. I was rather disappointed. Perhaps I had imagined that a fantastic team should come from a golden city, instead of one so grey and forlorn. Even the stadium of this invincible team was not up to much, being squashed in between housing with barely enough space to breathe. The stadium had a beautiful Greek name, the Filadelfia, which I had imagined from my ignorance in Buenos Aires to be a vast Colosseum gleaming in marble. Instead it was just a small grey box, the same colour as the city's factories. But every Sunday it became a volcano erupting with burgundy-coloured lava and brimming with shouts and noise. The loudest sounds came from a trumpet from which at various times came the signal for Torino to raise their game. Then the players in the burgundy shirts would go on the attack, and for a few moments the Filadelfia stadium was paradise.

The first time that I watched a match at the Filadelfia, Torino were playing against Novara. A club official came with me to the match, and he explained the tactics, formation, organisation and individual roles of the players. From the start Torino looked a well-organised team who had a fluent style of play, but they did not seem to be as extraordinary as their reputation suggested. After a few minutes in fact the away team scored, but the fans, including my guide, did not seem bothered at all.

"You"ll see," he said, "you"ll see when we really start to play.'

In my notebook, the same one in which I am writing now, I made a brief note: "Reminder for Mendez: can invincibility withstand defeat?" I must confess that my youthful presumption pushed me to jot that down, although writing now, the answer seems obvious. Greatness is something that people carry within them, and cannot be discerned unless you approach with humility. Wasn't this the same question Theseus put to himself before he entered the labyrinth?

I had come from Buenos Aires convinced that I already knew the secret of invincibility. It was only later that I really understood, after the start of the second half, when Bormida (that was the trumpeter's name) sounded the rallying call, making a shiver sweep through the thousands in the stadium provoking the awaited response from the team on the pitch.

"Look," said my Virgilesque guide, "now Valentino will attack." At once the style and sense of Torino's play began to take shape. You could hear the cry from Bacigalupo above the shouts from the terraces, as the ball was passed between Gabetto, Loik and Mazzola with a dreamlike ease. On the field power, joy, art and poetry existed in harmony. Confronted with such beauty, such perfection, those who witnessed it were aware of the void created as the world as they knew it slipped away in front of them. I reread again in my notebook that Torino scored four goals in just fifteen minutes as their opponents surrendered.

That evening in the silence of my room I made a further note. "Today I have really seen how all the points of the universe can be condensed into a gesture that, on the face of it, is just an ordinary game of football. I've witnessed infinite forms of reverence and infinite forms of anguish. But I do not know how to describe this."

I do not want to waffle on too much. For a month I followed the players in the squad, trying to understand what exactly was the secret of their strength. I interviewed players, club directors and officials and many others. Like Abenjacan in the Arabian fable, I was searching for one of life's secrets by questioning men, but the secret remained out of reach. Although the pages of my notebook were filled with words, my enquiry was a dry well.

Mendez sent me a telegram from Buenos Aires asking for news about my research and for a draft of my report. He seemed to be getting impatient, so I promised to send my report on 4 March. The day before, I was to travel to Lisbon with the team where they were to play a testimonial match for the great Benfica player Ferreira. The night before we left was spent in reading through the incredible statistics that told the story of the superiority of that team. Perhaps I was looking for the equation which the Swedish theorist had described.'

Don Ricca Tancredi gasped. Wasn't today 4 March? *That* 4 March? All at once his thoughts became confused in his mind, as though he had lost count of the figures he had been calculating. He shut the book and looked at the cover, anxiously turning it over and over in his hands. He tried to find a date of publication, where it had been published, a colophon, something that even told him in which year it had been published, but the burns prevented him from finding what he wanted. Don Ricca's heart was pounding as he read the last few lines:

'With great chivalry Torino allowed Ferreira and his Portuguese team the honour of winning the match. Even that defeat was a kind of triumph, a triumph of generosity. At Lisbon airport I went into a bookshop. I was in a foul mood as I looked for something to read in those last few hours before I had to write my difficult report for *El Gráfico*. There on a shelf as though waiting for me stood a book by my fellow Argentine, Jorge Luis Borges, entitled *The Invincibles*, which I bought without hesitation. I have always held the belief that it is books which choose their readers rather than vice versa. On the plane I settled myself into the back row alongside some Italian journalists. From there I could observe the Torino squad, as if in a last attempt to understand the secret of their invincibility. Soon afterwards I would start to make out what constituted invincibility, soon after I had started to read my book. On page seven, in the first chapter heading, I found the answer I had been searching for. "An unconsciousness of death makes people immortal. There is nothing very remarkable about being immortal. All creatures are immortal except for man."

So the signs of immortality in these men were almost imperceptible, flying as they were in a fragile plane which was carrying them, it was now clear to me, towards the disaster which would create their immortality.'

Don Ricca could not read any more. A strong emotion was

choking his throat. Once again he felt the flames burning his face and a tightness in his chest made him short of breath. Quickly he stood up and ran to the window to gulp in some fresh air. It was in that moment that he saw the huge black shape of a plane emerge out of the fog, as it ploughed into the wall of the Basilica above him.

What followed seemed to happen in a trance. A deafening roar filled the air, just as the sky was covered in thick red flames. Don Ricca raced outside as if crazed. He was the first to arrive at the scene of carnage, and he tried to edge close in the heat. Soon a few people from the village of Superga started to climb up the hill, frightened and shouting. From under a part of one of the plane's wings someone recovered a suitcase. Inside it contained some burgundy-coloured football shirts with the tricolour championship shield sewn onto the chest. The cries increased, together with desperate sobs, as the crowd realised the identity of the passengers.

Don Ricca had not needed the case to be opened in order to understand. Still short of breath he walked towards the wreckage and turned to the tail, which was rammed into the Basilica wall like a massive nail, near the remains of the plane's door which was half open. Carefully Don Ricca extracted something that was badly burnt and still smoking.

It was a book by Jorge Luis Borges, badly damaged and blackened by the fumes. He could just make out the title which read, *The Invincibles*.

Passerotto

On the morning of 20 January 1983 Jesus Joao Da Costa arrived at the Neurological Hospital in Alto Boavista exactly on time. It was his second day as a hospital nurse and he did not want to run the risk of being late. Even though it was still only a quarter to six, he had already crossed Rio de Janeiro, changing bus twice and running the last few metres on foot. As he reached the large entrance door he stopped for a moment, took a deep breath and let his eyes run along the length of the wall to the huge imposing building before him. Then he quickly plunged into the entrance hall as if diving into a pool of icy water. When he noticed his name stamped on the card in the machine for clocking on and off, he felt happy. He thought of his years of study, the hardships, the sacrifices made to get this job, and now as proof he saw his name printed in black on that pink card.

He quickly changed clothes and went to the ward, ready to receive orders for his shift. He listened carefully to Alberto Nuñes Coimbra who explained the developments of the previous night, and what action needed to be taken immediately: monitoring various treatments, taking essential samples, moving certain patients into the radiology department and dealing with the body of a patient who had died in the night.

Jesus made mental notes of what he had to do, exchanging a few words with some colleagues as he asked for their advice. Within a few moments he was so focused on his work that he had blocked out the world around him, as if his work was being conducted inside a dream. So when he found himself in room number seven, confronted by a man in tears, he could not be precisely sure how long the man had been there, immobile, unsure of what to do, crying silently with a pain that seemed as immense as a tidal wave.

During their preparatory training, nurses learn the most effective methods for dealing with acutely painful and unpleasant situations. It was perhaps a result of inexperience, or because the silence of the man's tears seemed to give him a powerful strength, that Jesus Da Costa felt dumbstruck, rooted to the spot, only able to watch. In fact it was the man in tears who noticed him and offered the first few words.

'I wasn't able to look after him,' the man said through his tears. 'It's all my fault.'

The nurse suddenly felt a deep sense of pity. It was not only because of the pale swollen face of the dead man visible above the sheet, but it came from the atmosphere in the room, from the peeling paint on the bed frame, from the harsh neon light, from the paltry objects lying on the desk: an apple, a bottle of water and an old portable radio. Jesus searched inside himself for a phrase or gesture to break his embarrassment, so he walked towards the body and read the chart on the end of the bed: 'Manuel Francisco dos Santos, 50 years old – Pau Grande.' He glanced quickly at the medical details, and with a strong voice and his chest erect he took refuge in the most professional expression he had learnt:

'Unfortunately there was nothing that could be done; I don't think it was anybody's fault sir. He was very ill.'

But the man in tears did not seem to have heard this weak explanation.

'I should have looked after him better,' he said. 'Mané was like a child.'

With this he turned to look at the dead man, and from his eyes, which Jesus noticed were sky blue, fell two teardrops the size of walnuts. Slowly he dried his face with his hand and carried on talking in a veiled voice.

'When I first started to notice him he really was just a lad, no more than five or six years old,' he said, looking the nurse in the eye as if he were about to reveal a secret. 'I had just finished looking after an old chap at Minas Gerais so I was on the lookout for someone new. As I was not usually in that part of Rio I decided to look around the streets and, towards the forest, I arrived at Pau Grande. Fifty years ago it was even worse than today, a place covered in dust and misery. After the rains, came the risk of drowning in the mud. On the day I arrived, the streets were full of kids playing, just like all Brazilian kids. They played with a ball made of rags. And this was how I met Mané.'

The man seemed to have been given new heart as he thought of these memories, and his tone of voice seemed stronger, so much so that Jesus, almost without noticing it, sat down on the edge of the bed and began to listen.

'Mané would stay on his own, to one side, watching the others chasing after the ball. He had two crooked skinny legs like those of a sparrow; two feeble sticks that would never have enough strength to run. Yet he kept smiling. As he sat on the sidelines, his veiled eyes followed the other kids playing. He always smiled and he seemed happy. Around him was dust and huts, but nobody took any notice of that poor twisted little bird. So I thought to myself it is not worth going on into Rio. I'll stop here and be the guardian angel to a little sparrow, a *passerotto*.' [1]

As he thought of this, the man nodded to himself, and Jesus Da Costa started to feel sympathy for him, and even some relief, for the man's crying had ceased, to be replaced by the satisfaction of telling his story. So Jesus said nothing as he let the words flow over him.

'Poliomyelitis. Although the people had very little in Pau Grande, they didn't go without polio, which had so ravaged Passerotto's legs. But this didn't seem to bother Mané. He was always happy, even with his discomfort, even if he could only walk awkwardly for a short way and could not run after the ball like the others. When his father saw how small and bent he was, he would get a lump in his throat. It was to soothe that pain in some way that I managed to convince him to take his son to a doctor in Rio. Deamaro put him on his shoulders with me by his side, and we went to talk to this doctor who operated on children with damaged legs. The doctor took him, and for hours he was under the knife as efforts were made to straighten out those legs. The surgery only managed to half straighten them, so when he

1 *Passerotto* in Italian is literally little sparrow. *Garrincha* in the Portuguese of North Eastern Brazil means wren.

returned the doctor was wearing a rather sheepish look on his face. He said that at least his left leg would be able to walk.

That night Deamaro could not sleep, and I kept him company for hours as I learnt how much a man could cry, for the suffering of giving life to a *passerotto* with crooked legs. Deamaro would cry and shout at the heavens. He drank beer and shook his fists at the moon, while I racked my brains to try and find some remedy. Next morning we went to the market in Julinha where I bought an old iron tricycle for a few *cruzeiros*. Back at home we tied Mané's feet to the pedals, and he went off for a spin around the dust of Pau Grande on that strange contraption. As he pedalled he smiled. Pedalling behind the other kids made him feel happy. Even though they rather made fun of him, he still pedalled and smiled. By and by his legs became stronger, and as he got down from the tricycle he stood more firmly on his feet. Sometimes he even ran.

One day in July I was with Mané as usual watching the kids play football. The ball rolled towards us, and when Joao Paolo Pirinha, out of spite, shouted at Mané to kick it back, I saw the happiness disappear from his eyes. He turned towards Joao Paolo and shouted to him to come and get the ball himself, then a smile reappeared on his lips. But I could tell that inside his nerves were jangling. When I looked at him again he seemed calmer. He had the ball at his feet as he wiped the palms of his hands on his shorts, waiting for Pirinha. I was next to him, and I kept hold of his arm as Pirinha slowly came up and stood still opposite Mané. I squeezed his arm harder, and perhaps Passerotto understood something as he stared into his opponent's eyes, before he feinted to the left, leaning on my side, while Joao Paulo stretched out his leg to get the ball, he shot away in the opposite direction with the ball between his legs and a big smile on his lips. From that day on, no one could take the ball off him, because each time Mané would lean on my side, and then dart off smiling in the other direction. The people were entertained by this display, and fascinated by Mané's kind of improvised dance. So they simply came to call him Garrincha, which is a local word for a wren.'

Jesus gave a start. What on earth was this man talking about? For a moment he felt uneasy, as if confronted by a madman, but he noticed once again that those blue eyes had filled with tears, and he realised that this man was perfectly sane. He stood up and went towards the body in the bed, looking at the man's features that had been contorted in death. Little by little, as if from a dream, there emerged the face of someone he recognised, the same face from the photo which his father had kept on the door of his barber's shop: those eyebrows, and the pronounced cheek bones; the eyes and mouth of a champion. Jesus was engulfed by a flood of colour, a powerful emotion and faces and noises from old memories. And he understood that this was not a moment to ask questions.

'Pele's legs were perfect, toned, sinuous and shining, as though designed by Michelangelo,' said the man in tears. He gestured to the bed as he continued. 'On the other hand, Mané's legs were two living sticks, twisted like the destiny of the dispossessed, a madman's joke, making fun of their existence. They were the same as the legs of the street urchins from the *favelas*² which is why they loved him so much. Those ugly sticks conned every opponent, and ran on with happiness to many victories. His legs would go one way, as Mané and the ball went the other, while from the stands a huge shout of joy went up from his people, who ran with him up the touchline before he crossed the ball to set up another goal.

Passerotto always appreciated simple things, and for this reason his game was always based on simplicity: always the same feint, the same quick dancer's move down the right, and the square ball to the centre which the crowds so loved.

Sometimes he would make you feel sad. When you saw the strength of Vava, or the inspiration of Pele, you asked yourself how on earth he could play at all. One day during training, gathering up the ball and his courage, he stood opposite *O' Rey*³, so small and crooked in comparison to *O 'Rey's* poise. He looked him in the eye and said: "Excuse me, I don't know how to do acrobatics, I don't head the ball with power and I'm not that strong. All I have is that

2 *favelas*: shanty towns
3 'O' Rey': the King, a nickname for Pele

51

dummy. I look at the opponent, and I'm off, he falls over as I shoot away. I always do the same trick, nothing else." I saw Pele with his beautiful smile, go over to my little sparrow and put an arm round his shoulder. "You don't have to justify anything Mané," he said to him, "because dribbling with the ball is your bread and butter. It is a simple thing, but the team and I depend on it." Mané looked down at his crooked legs, then he looked at that perfect face opposite him, and he gave his lethal dummy, running off down the touchline with the ball stuck to his feet, leaving Pele staring into space.'

A smile broke across the man's face, as for several moments he fixed his gaze on a point far away from that cold room. He stretched a little saying:

'Together, we really had some fun. No one could understand how he could do that dummy. People studied it, discussed it, wrote theories about it, certain they had found the right answer, but when they saw that move again the theories collapsed like a house of cards. They looked at his knees, one of which bent inwards, the other turned out; they would watch his legs go one way, before he burst off in the other direction with the ball, as the opponents remained immobile, bewitched, and sitting on their arses. Defenders sometimes dealt with him roughly, kicking his ankles in an attempt to frighten him, but he carried on as though nothing had happened, with that dance fashioned from that one feint.

Once we played against an English team who had a full back called Wilson, who was instructed to follow Mané as if he was his shadow, to allow him no breathing space and give him a few whacks if necessary, which is exactly what he did. Dig and run, run and dig, I'd never seen anything like it before. How Mané suffered; he would get knocked over and be straight back up; he would run and try to shake off this demon, gritting his teeth until eventually his smile disappeared. Then at a certain point in the match I watched him escape in one of his sprints. He would sway and do his dummy, without touching the ball which stayed still where it was. He shot off as usual with Wilson hacking at his ankles for a few yards, unable to reach the ball, until the Englishman gave him a vicious challenge which brought him down. This time Mané stood up slowly, and turning back down the pitch, he picked up the ball with a smile and offered it to his opponent, who was only able to mumble a feeble "I'm sorry," with his head down in mortification. After that Wilson did not have the heart to keep kicking Mané, who carried on with his famous dummy, even scoring two goals.'

Jesus Da Costa kept silent as he listened, fascinated by stories that brought to mind another era, stories he could remember people enjoying telling about the life of the great Garrincha. He remembered the incredible deeds of a strong, spectacular team from when he was a child. People used to say they could perform legendary feats, not those of mortal men. In his mind's eye he saw again the tears of joy on the faces of his father and brothers, the photos of footballers kitted out in gold and green which were paraded through the streets during the improvised carnivals that would start up after a victory. Now he found himself by that lifeless body, and that strange man who continued to speak as though in a trance.

Memories can sometimes strike you powerfully, burning you painfully because, in an instant, words, smells and sounds can return, things which have been put aside because of the urgency required to live in the present. Then they start to nudge you again, scraping and yelling as if they were young and fresh. So it was that Jesus Joao Da Costa felt surprised by that wave of memories that he thought had been forgotten, amazed at how he had been able to forget them so easily. He felt regret that the others had not warned him about that chunk of the past, left to die alone in a hospital room, without the dignity of the prayerful vigil that he deserved.

With this sentiment, suspended between sorrow and shame, Jesus Da Costa found himself wondering how Garrincha had come to die in this way, how the people had forgotten his *alegria*,[4] and had abandoned him. As though he had read his mind, the man began speaking again.

'Mané never forgot Pau Grande and the shanty towns, even when he was famous and was a world champion, revered like a deity. He

---

4 *alegria*: Portuguese for 'lust for life', 'joie de vivre'

53

would often return to his people bringing gifts and cruzeiros, and play football in the streets, sometimes showing his magical feint, as the children danced and laughed because that devastating move brought them happiness. Everyone, as in the stadium, called it l'alegria do povo.

Listen, I can honestly say to you that Mané never became cynical or angry, but always stayed the same Passerotto we all knew. It may be hard for you to understand, but the day Deamaro took him to have his legs straightened, Mané remained silent on his father's shoulders as we went down those dusty streets towards Rio. I just watched and listened, as a guardian angel must do. And from those shoulders I am sure, Passerotto dreamt of being able to fly, of being able to run like Joao Pirinha. So it was for this reason that he never fully understood all the riches and glory, while Pele (with the gleaming legs, sculpted from marble) travels the world shaking hands and slapping backs. For Mané it was enough to run and make that magical dummy to feel freedom, because for a little bird like him, being free was the most important thing in the world. All the rest did not matter, it was no more than the shouts and empty words of distracted people, people who didn't remember him, because they were incapable of remembering anything.

Nowadays they say that Mané was foolish, gullible and even unintelligent. Once he threw away a portable radio he had bought in Sweden. Santos had asked him how the hell he could understand a radio which only spoke Swedish, when he knew only a smattering of Portuguese. Perhaps it was true when people said he lost his way chasing after women, like a child running after something in a fairy tale. But those that said it were the kind who never remembered being children, and never believed in fairy tales anyway. They would say he was an idiot, that he was guilty of throwing away his own life, by living off old memories and alcohol. The ones who said this were the ones who would forget everything, while my Passerotto remembered everything, and when you are unable to forget, life can become a heavy burden. To see him deteriorate was as sour as the aftertaste of a heavy night on the town, as he continued with that dummy, though his stomach was bloated and he was long in the tooth. Believe me, it is all too easy for people to forget, otherwise my Passerotto would not now be so alone in this icy room.

Mané never forgot anything. I remember the day when the Prime Minister invited the whole World Cup winning team to his palace for them to collect an award. Amidst the plush carpets and precious vases Vava and Nilton Santos turned up, giving each other nudges with their elbows as they gazed around in amazement. Pele was there smiling serenely as usual. Jose Altafini, known as Mazola, was there and so was the full back Bellini with tears in his eyes. And I was there too, steering Mané round the room, and for once he had no need for his famous dummy.

When the Prime Minister started his speech, everyone held their breath, listening silently to the eulogy about the honour they had brought to Brazil. Everyone continued to hold their breath as the Prime Minister added that each of the national heroes was to receive a gift, and they could not restrain their joy when they learned that each was to receive a villa in Copacabana. Only my Passerotto kept quiet. The Prime Minister noticed this, and asked if the great Garrincha would prefer a different gift. "Do you want money? What else would you prefer?" he asked. I smiled to myself because by now I understood, but the Prime Minister had a rather worried expression on his face as he questioned Passerotto, who eventually stammered timidly: "What I would really like sir, would be for you to release that little bird who is in the cage over your shoulder. Please sir, let him go." Mané never forgot anything. Once he met up again with Pirinha, giving him the American car he had only just bought, which was poppy red, and as long as an ocean liner. So you would see poverty and wealth side by side in Pau Grande, Joao Paul Pirinha pulling away in a six-metre long Cadillac, toothless and smiling, on the unmade forest road. Such a scene is absolute joy. Mané consumed happiness day after day like a child sucking on a never-ending sweet. No one can tell a passerotto what to do.'

The voice became silent, and time seemed to flee from the room, as the words drowned Jesus Da Costa in a wave of melancholy. Thoughts attacked the nurse, confusing because of their meaning and because of the way in which the stories had unfolded. It was as he tried to put his reasoning in some kind of order that the door of the room opened and he heard Luisinho Mora call him in an angry tone of voice. With a stern face his colleague reproached him:

'What have I got to do round here to get a body taken to the mortuary?'

Jesus Da Costa shook himself and mumbled an excuse. He was just about to offer some explanation about his conversation with the man in tears, about how he had felt the need to listen to him in his distress, when all of a sudden he stopped and realised that the man had disappeared without a trace. Anxiously, he ran to the door and out into the corridor, but he could only see Luisinho Mora pushing a bed, his face still angry, who curtly asked him to take care of the dead body.

Jesus Da Costa returned to the bed where he helped a colleague prepare the lifeless body. Confusion swirled inside Da Costa's head. He thought of the stories he had just heard, of how that man had both moved and unsettled him at the same time. He spoke to the other nurse who was bending down, arranging the bed:

'Did you know that this was Mané Garrincha?'

He paused for a moment, before he lifted the sheet and cast a glance at swollen body of the champion, and he grimaced murmuring almost to himself: 'Maybe he was Garrincha once, but he died a poor fool.'

After saying this he wheeled the bed out of the room, reminding the lad to hurry up, because the day was beginning and they had not yet done any work.

The Wrong Colour

On the morning of 5 April 1915 Jack Johnson was dreaming of being a boy once again in Galveston Texas. He was helping his father unload sacks of rice from a ship in the dock, a ship which seemed both large and small at the same time. The air was sticky, and he moved wearily as if each step required a tremendous effort, but he still worked at a good speed and in a few minutes had managed to unload the hold on his own. So he sat down and looked at the ship, enormous once more, and he looked at his little hands and he felt an incredible force within himself: in that moment he seemed to be glowing and sculpted from marble. On the boy's face spread the smile so hated by many, and he saw the faces of his opponents, broken, racked with fatigue and punches, hundreds of eyes swollen by his blows. He smiled, but deep in his heart he was uneasy. It was then that the brightness of the sun dazzled him. With the slow motion of a dream he brought a hand to his forehead, and on the horizon he could make out the black shape of his father. As if he had read his thought the shadow said, 'Jack, you're the wrong colour.'

He looked at his skin but did not understand. He looked at his invincible hands and his perfect torso, sculpted in a gleaming chocolate colour.

Dreams do not have the limits of our normal logic. Treacherously they come and go, changing in place and time. That morning as he listened to the shadow of his father on the pavement in Galveston, Jack Johnson saw Tommy Burns laid out at his feet. His face was swollen and his nose bleeding. He saw Jack London watching from the side of the ring and he shouted out with a thunderous roar. After this Johnson remained in silence, dumbstruck by the shock. He had wanted to teach that foppish writer a lesson, but instead he stayed silent and smelt his breath which reeked of bourbon, hearing his repeated call from the pages of the newspapers, 'Someone must do something to wipe that smile from Johnson's face. The white man must be saved.'

London took a step forward and swung a tremendous hook at his body, then another at his jaw and others which resonated in the air with the same noise as a hammer on wood. Johnson shot off and sat on his bed to recover from the pain of the blows. He looked around but there was no trace of his adversary, though the blows continued to thud against his bedroom door. When he threw open the door he saw Buddy Miles looking worried and completely soaked with sweat.

They went out into the fresh morning air for the usual training run, jogging on the Malecon. The sun shone on the water and gave a pinkish tint to Havana's old houses. The boxer stopped for a moment to appreciate this scene, fascinated by the quality of the light. In the softness of the light the city now appeared far away from him, the same city where he would fight against Jessie Willard that afternoon. With this thought the body of his opponent materialised in front of him and sneered as his voice actually began to speak.

'I'll break you into pieces, you black ugly mug,' said the Texan. 'I'll carry off your title and that coal that you carry about with you.'

In a flash Jack shook himself like a man possessed, leaning to the left while letting go a massive hook from the opposite side. The image of Willard staggered as Jack's other fist landed, straightening him up as a hail of punches swept over his chin until, completely defenceless, he was spread out on the ground. Johnson only stopped swinging his arms in front of him when he felt a hand on his shoulder and heard the voice of Buddy Miles repeating the words:

'Calm yourself boy, it's just the wind.'

The heavyweight stopped. Like a steam vehicle powered by pressure, he gave a few deep snorts. But he smiled. He thought of the curious nature of time which moves close and then moves away like a punch ball in training sessions. He thought of Buddy calling him 'boy', though of course he was a boy no longer. Jack Johnson was already thirty-seven years old, but of lives he had already had at least a dozen. On his head weighed a sentence he was to serve, a punishment for violating the 'Mann Act'. Jack Johnson, a frequenter of prostitutes, had already been married twice to white women, making him pilloried – a criminal who had to flee.

A champion is not scared by the adversary as he climbs into the ring, not much anyway. In the middle of the ring there are rules, although courage and strength are always put to the test. There is a referee; there are punches; there is your life before you. Everything is there, everything is in the balance. The hardest battle is fought outside the ropes, where others always make the rules and punches can swing in the air to no result. If you are a man of the wrong colour the rounds can extend infinitely, even above the forty-five scheduled for the bout with Tommy Burns or against Willard that afternoon. If you are a man at the top of the world, with a Dusemberg Sport, always sharply dressed, then the rules are not fixed so securely.

On the night of 4 September 1912 Johnson, as was his right, defended his World Title against Jim Flynn. By this time he had already squashed Burns and humiliated James Jeffries, both of them men as white as bread. He caused a sensation with his unbeatable technique, for the women he had loved. Beautiful women, but their skin colour was too pale. A few hours before the fight a man with a face like a cowboy sidled up to the champion and put an envelope in his hand.

'Some friends of mine sent me this. Can you read Johnson, or do you need some help?'

Jack opened the letter and read: 'Fall to the canvas or we'll make you swing from a tree. You choose, coward. Your fate is sealed. Signed: the Ku Klux Klan.' When he raised his head, the emissary had vanished, and his anger was just starting to boil.

Flynn put up resistance for nine rounds. He was a big heavy lump of wood. At the *Dog and Cat* they called him 'the rock'. He probably did not understand the reason for all the fury. Those present at the fight remembered the look of fear in his eyes. There was no chance of him putting out his hand to ask for help from someone as he floundered against the ropes. He had the expression of a lamb awaiting the slaughter. Six policemen went into the ring to stop the fists which continued to rain down blows as the referee struggled to declare the fight over, frantically waving his arms like a bird. The people shouted, divided between acclaiming the winner and rage against the black man who was champion once again. They wondered what the hell Jack was waiting for as he stayed on his feet in the ring after the massacre. He stood fixed in the middle of the square for half an hour, the champion. His smile fixed like a sneer as he turned about the ring with a delirious look.

'I've read your message,' he said to himself, 'I'm waiting for you. Come on out then because I have only just started.'

On that April afternoon in Havana which we are talking about there was once again a title in the balance; once again a life in the balance. The day before, a distinguished lawyer from Chicago arrived in a black car. He did not leave any letter, he made no threatening gesture. He was no rough cowboy, he was an advocate. Someone else had already prepared the chess board, and he was required to make the final move. He ordered a glass of port, took a taste and raised it to the light to appreciate the colour. Then he made a play of words giving the champion the prospect of avoiding his problems, of escaping from the sentence in a stuffy prison cell where little light enters and the days move at a deadly pace. He put a hand in one of the pockets of his expensive jacket, took out a notebook and wrote down a figure. The sentence could be annulled and he could put a good few dollars in the bank. There was a possibility for Jack to return home and leave the life of a wandering showman. He made the offer with a cheerful smile, like an estate agent who invites his client to think a while before making a decision. Tearing off the sheet of paper with the jotted figure he passed it to Johnson then stood up and, touching the brim of his hat with two fingers, almost gave a bow.

'America will finally have its rightful champion,' he said, 'and you can go and enjoy life in peace.'

In a flash he disappeared inside the black car while Jack remained alone at the table.

The ring formed a small part of the arena, raised up on a sort of dais. The ropes were tied to large stake-like pivots fixed on rough wooden beams used for railway sleepers. The boxers move towards the dais by cutting through the crowd like an ice-breaker in an ice-floe. They leave behind their whole life and their fears. In that moment they are like a bull ready for battle. They see the ring with a mixture of love and hate. Up there between the ropes there is no way of escape, and at times the reckoning can be fatal. Sometimes they will imagine or even dream about the end of the fight. To Jack Johnson that afternoon the ring seemed like a sacrificial altar.

Willard was a rude cowboy, an arrogant boaster trying to become champion. Apart from that he was as white as milk and a clever boxer who knew how to take a beating or punch hard at the right moment. The bout was scheduled for an interminable forty-five rounds. As a result it started with the sun high in the sky, and the town square throbbing with men wearing hats. Only a few women were about. There were mainly distinguished men, 'WASPS' wearing top hats or Yankees in straw boaters, fidgeting at ringside, shouting to Willard:

'Murder the black bear!'

Johnson started fencing as always. Except for rare exceptions he preferred fencing, the thrill and the tactics rather than brute force. He searched for the decisive blow only when he was sure that his opponent was close to the end. That afternoon he conducted the first twenty-five rounds without exerting himself too much. The air was hot and the shouts of the crowd pushed him against his opponent who, minute by minute, fought with a little less passion.

In his corner during the break before the twenty-sixth round Jack had no wish to listen to the advice of his trainer. He called over to Buddy Miles, looked him in the eye and said:

'Get my wife and children out of this place. Do it quickly.'

Buddy smiled, convinced that the champion was tiring and had decided to resolve the contest in the swiftest possible way, well before the end. It would be a spectacle too cruel for sensitive eyes. So he nodded to say that he understood and went over to whisper right in the woman's ear. Then he turned towards Jack and gave a thumbs up gesture to explain that it was taken care of.

Instead of launching himself against his adversary and battering him as he had done with Burns and Jeffries years earlier, the champion stood up as though a veil had dropped across his face. A sudden fatigue seemed to slow him down. Willard's first few punches stopped him in his tracks. He threw a couple of half-hearted right hands and then took a series of blows to the chin that seemed to stun him. The crowd went delirious, shouting with joy as they saw Johnson stagger against the ropes, while an incredulous Willard appraised the scene almost unable to believe his own eyes.

Jack fell to the canvas, but not with a giant thud. He went down slowly like a football with a hole in it, folding in on himself before he lay down on the ground. The referee leaned over him and then started to count for ten seconds that seemed to last for a month. Finally he gave a definitive gesture with his arm to declare the end of the war, raising Willard's glove as the smile of a champion spread across his lips.

In the pandemonium that followed, few noticed that Johnson was lying on his back in a comfortable position as if he was having a rest, rather than in the immobile pose of a broken man. He smiled peacefully with his usual expression and above his head he kept an arm raised to shield his eyes from the glare of the Havana sun. He turned towards the changing rooms with a dressing-gown round his shoulders. Around him people jeered and shouted his obituary into the sky. Buddy Miles was next to him carrying the towel and the bucket like a heavy load, trying to hold back his tears with great difficulty.

'It's time to go home,' he said, 'it's time to go home old chum.'

Nobody paid Jack the debt. After the fight the lawyer was nowhere to be seen and the verbal assurances made over a glass of port disappeared in a moment like snow melting in the sunshine. In these matters there are no contracts – just an act of good faith, an agreement between gentlemen. It is your word that counts, and as the wise well know, a word can fly away. Together with the word flew fifty thousand dollars and the hope of avoiding a prison sentence. The champion's exile would continue for some time while hiding with Buddy in some part of Europe as his mother began to fall ill. Climbing into French, Spanish and Latin American rings, he would exchange knocks with anyone to be assured of a decent purse which would make ends meet. Sometimes he would fight twice in one day and would keep going into the night playing a double bass the size of a wardrobe.

In any place, even in Patagonia so they say, he would challenge anyone with his boastful smile that made him so hated. No one could put up much resistance against his champion's class: the left hook to the temple; the danced half step to the right; the move around and in front, to bring an upper cut to the chin. He moved about the world giving lessons.

In the autumn of '28, against an anonymous opponent, all of a sudden the world seemed too big to Jack. Raising his arm for a punch his fist felt heavy, his legs as hard as marble and he felt a cold sweat on his skin. Between the sixth and seventh rounds he saw Buddy Miles approaching the corner with his hobbling gait. He had the towel on his shoulders and a bucket in his hands and he really did not seem dead. He passed the sponge over his face and gave him the usual advice, miming a left hook to be quickly repeated from underneath. After the bell, as Flanagan shook him to go back into the ring, Jack saw Miles go down again among the public towards his mother in the front row, where he helped her up and turned her towards him to wave. That same night Johnson's mother died and, a few days later, the wanderer with the boastful smile returned to his homeland where he let himself be still.

The following years were not exhilarating. Exhilarating means victory and success rather than gaol and the little left of your life afterwards. However it was still a form of life and Jack knew how to enjoy it. Even if one did not see him so often at the wheel of a Dusemberg Sport he continued to indulge his pleasures, fighting rounds with respect for the old rules. He did not always follow rules, sometimes following those darker leanings of human existence instead.

One day he met his friend Sam McVey, an old heavyweight to whom he had taught a severe lesson some years earlier. Sam was ill, sad and badly dressed, drifting like so many former champions forgotten by the world.

'I'm dying Jack. I'm desperate. I don't even have a place while I'm alive leave alone when I'm dead,' he said through his tears. At this Jack knew what he must do. He gathered the last scraps of cash that he had saved and accompanied Sam to a funeral parlour to buy a decent coffin.

June 10 1946, in Raleigh North Carolina, was a beautiful day and Johnson had an appointment with a journalist from the *New York Times*. He drove an old Ford which was strangely modest for him, a car as anonymous and black as a lump of coal.

He drove fast because he was late as usual. At sixty-eight years old he had not lost his taste for chasing pretty girls, especially if they were fair skinned. In a restaurant where he had stopped for a glass of beer he had joked with a waitress named Bella.

'That's the same name as the prostitute I got into trouble with,' he said, and he started to tell the story of how thirty years earlier they had found a way to throw him out of his home town. He then showed her a few boxing moves, and let her touch his arm which, even at his age, was still like a tree trunk. Then he promised her that he would invite her to the ringside in a few weeks' time for one of the exhibitions he still gave where he taught the real art of boxing. He would ask Joe Jeanette, with whom he had boxed six weeks earlier; sending the crowd wild as they applauded, as if he was a young lad making his debut.

The car drove on towards the appointment and, perhaps in preparation for the interview, Jack mentally went through his life. He saw his mother who called him 'coward' as a child because he would avoid the scraps with his friends. He heard the same insult shouted by the crowd after one of his victories. Jack could see himself small and thin in the cotton fields where he had helped his grandparents, and then he saw himself as an older, tougher boy with a sack of jute on his back at the port in Galveston with his father. He saw the faces of the men with whom he had locked horns, powerful men like Marvin Hart, Bob Fitzsimmons, Sam Langford and again Joe Jeanette who he had fought eight times. As he skidded along the tarmac in that small vehicle Buddy Miles' tears after Havana once again materialised and that memory brought to mind the smile of the lawyer who had promised him money and freedom in exchange for a defeat that continued to burn in his stomach like a knife wound. 'A life like that,' he thought, 'you couldn't make it up. How can I explain to a Yankee writer what it means to be a champion of the wrong colour? A life like that can only be dreamt, battled with throughout the night when you are asleep, in an encounter of sixteen thousand rounds.'

In the small space of the car, Jack Johnson's interminable battles became condensed, like a thick impenetrable fog that clouds across the eyes. The road on which he sped led into Madison Street, with a wide crossroads full of rush-hour traffic. The lights in Johnson's direction were fixed on red as the champion drove on, immersed in recollections.

He did not see, or saw badly, or perhaps he saw the wrong colour, for he hit a lorry full on, giving him the knockout punch which took away his life.

The first people on the scene who extracted his dead body from the wreckage commented that his face still wore the smile of a boastful black man – the same indelible mark of a champion.

Nuvola

On 20 October 1930, Tazio Nuvolari left Mantua for a test drive in his Alfa Romeo 1750. It was a calm day and the Alfa responded instantly as he pressed it to accelerate, giving him a deep sense of satisfaction. Tazio felt content, as the past year had been very successful. He had won several races, including the Mille Miglia, where he had the satisfaction of beating his adversary Varzi after a great struggle. As they tore through Ancona he had felt tense, a good minute behind Achille. During each refuelling stop he had asked his mechanics if he could unleash the full power of his car, only to be told to wait, to preserve the engine and bide his time. Being told to wait when in full flight was frustrating for Nuvolari who would rather crash than allow himself to be overtaken.

As they arrived in the city centre, under the Conero, Tazio pondered the situation with a heavy heart. 'I can just about come to terms with defeat,' he thought, 'when everything goes wrong, or when I feel my arms are unable to steer the car through the bends as they should. But here the tone of the engine is as sweet as an orchestra and if I put my foot down I'll leave the others behind.' So he glanced at his watch, considering the countless roads he still had to negotiate, and to keep himself composed he said out loud that preserving the car was the intelligent thing to do, a wise move, a sound tactic. Yet in the same moment in which he convinced himself of the value of being prudent, from somewhere in his senses, from within his hands, with a strange smell in his nostrils, he felt the air to be crackling with the thrill of speed which captivated him and he once again raced on like a man possessed.

At Ancona he stopped for a break and, with fists and teeth clenched, he animatedly discussed his position with his team. Together the mechanics and driver had reached this point where the race was going smoothly enough, except for the fact that Varzi was over a minute ahead and his team were telling him to wait.

'I'm the one,' he said almost shouting, 'who knows when to press on; it's me who sets the limits, I'm the explorer here.'

The mechanics stood and looked at each other, not quite sure how to react. To them the car is purely mechanical; it is formed by scientific methods; it is run by a gearing system that is part of a design which follows a specific theory; so many revolutions per minute, so much resistance. The calculations are always exact, two plus two always equals four. The mathematics were a blessing, but here in front of them was this champion with tunnel vision who was locked in a tussle with his adversary, and whose pride told him in each race to show everyone who was the greatest. In front of them was Nuvolari, shouting, with a look of thunder in his eye. The man was almost a legend already. They felt a mixture of fear and respect for that small man, kitted out like an aviator, and so they gave him their assent, telling him to push on, to use every ounce of the car's potential without saying anything and, of course, Nuvolari would leave nothing in reserve. He would exhaust himself as well as the car in his chase.

Years later, as he closed his eyes in a dream, he could see the bends and straights from Ancona being eaten up in his chase, swallowed in the dark night, torn by the headlamps, a truly horrible dream where the real world was always present at the edge of the road, out of focus and disfigured by the speed of the Alfa. He caught up with the enemy just after Peschiera, where he had homed in like a hunter who keeps the life of a pheasant in suspense, before making the instant decision for life or for death.

'You won't escape, my little prince,' he said grinding his teeth, 'I'll overtake at top speed and you won't see me again till we get to Brescia. I'll be in the restaurant waiting for you.'

Squeezing the claxon as he said this, Tazio overtook like a rocket. From behind his window, Varzi offered a weak smile. He would really have preferred to escape off the road and hide.

On that afternoon of 30 October 1930, as the Alfa tore across the plain, Nuvolari steered his mind through various memories. He thought about the past, of the great things he had done, of his races that were now almost legendary and the future that still promised so much. He loved racing, he loved to fly, and with his red car flying over the plain he would have liked to see the towns from above, then swoop low, and rise again to the height of the clouds flying quickly in the sky, able to feel unlimited freedom to go wherever he wanted.

He remembered the time as a boy when he had bought the wreck of a Bleriot from a workshop. With his friend Paoletto Rossini they had put the pieces of the biplane together, but it was never any good for actual flying. Panting, they dragged it along over the field, making it seem more of a dead weight than a swift aeroplane. Paoletto wanted to give up, but Tazio showed the tenacity for which he was later to become so renowned. With an ingenious contraption consisting of some rope and a pulley, they managed to raise the feeble plane above the roof of the farm. By some miracle it managed to arrive up on top of the building, in an attempt to take a leap towards the clouds that were visible above. Then Tazio started the engine and gave his friend the signal to let go of the rope.

'This is a plane,' he shouted as he prepared for the launch, 'so it must fly whether it wants to or not!'

The flight lasted the time it takes to say 'amen'. The engine made a gloriously desperate roar as Bleriot finished, minus dignity, in a hay-loft, amidst the shouts and laughter of the people around. In the confusion of bleating mules, frightened hens and flying hay, beneath a pile of hay bales, two tears of fury slipped down Tazio's cheek. The tears were certainly a result of his shame and embarrassment, but also because he had so far been unable to reach the clouds above.

Moving back and forth through memories is rather like driving, like turning through a chicane or repeating the ups and downs of a conversation. As you try to brake or change gear, your thoughts can quickly slide on something, and you find yourself spinning back to front. This was exactly the sensation Tazio felt as he drove on, lost in old memories. When he snapped out of his thoughts, he realised that he was well past Mantua, and was now much further on to the south. He was in Reggio Emilia and it was getting late. The sky which had been clear blue had turned a gloomy wintry grey, and some large raindrops were already starting to fall on the asphalt road.

'I must be mad,' the champion thought, 'to get myself soaked when I'm only out for a practice run. I let myself fall asleep like an idiot.' He had put in the right amount of petrol and tuned the car to start the journey home, but the rain started to fall heavily and the road was quickly becoming a river.

It was hard to see the road ahead through the storm, and Nuvolari's car made a couple of skids, as it was hard even for a champion to keep it balanced in those conditions. If a car loses control it is difficult for the most skilled drivers to handle it, for there is sometimes no escape from the inevitable. Maybe because of the water, the Alfa's engine gave a couple of spluttering noises as if it had caught a cold, then it started to cough and slowed down, forcing Tazio to pull over to the side of the road.

From where he had stopped, Nuvolari noticed a huge, carved wooden door, which seemed to give onto a large entrance hall. So he quickly moved over the road to take shelter from the storm. The sign on the door showed that this was a monastery, and the champion decided to knock. From within he heard a voice asking who it was that was calling for help and he replied, 'It's Tazio Nuvolari, the racing driver. My car has broken down, and I'm soaked to the skin.' Then he added, 'I just want some shelter until this storm blows over.'

The door was opened wide by a bearded monk wearing a cowl and a broad smile.

'If this is hell then we're all right,' said the friar. 'It's only an argument in the clouds, just a cloudburst.' he said gesturing to the champion to come in. Then he looked him in the eye and said:

'Nuvolari? You'll have to excuse me but I've never heard that name before. We are a shy group of people who have consciously retreated from the world, we have little curiosity. So you are a driver. I suppose you drive cars which compete in races,' he said, stopping to take in Nuvolari as if he had never before seen anything so strange. The friar had a smile playing on his lips, and his head was shaking slightly as he wondered whether this creature dressed in leathers was really human.

Tazio stiffened. Inside he felt his wounded pride start to stir a foul temper. He had had great days of glory, he had triumphed in the most beautiful of races where people lined the roads in a kind of dream. Thousands of Italians would wait through the night, in the cold and the wet if need be, to see a motor car flash past, to hear that roar, to glimpse underneath the leather crash helmet, under the goggles, the adored face of a great champion. They would point with their fingers and shout his name imagining they were racing at a hundred miles per hour in that same rocket. The whole of Italy had hailed him. Photographs in the newspapers, radio reports, and weeks later people were still talking about his achievements. But now this smiling friar appeared to know nothing of his fame, as though all that publicity meant absolutely nothing inside the walls of the community. He was just another eccentric. A driver, he supposed!

Nuvolari wanted to reply that he was a symbol of the modern age, that for many he was a hero built with panache and courage. In life you can choose to set yourself apart, to contemplate the spirit and the divine, but there is also the tangible, the metal to make a powerful machine with which you can battle against your adversaries. It was true that outside where it rains so often it is a kind of hell. A place of mud, black exhaust fumes and of a grease which can stain even the whitest soul. Nuvolari's pride wanted to say all this, but they had reached a spacious room, rather spartan in appearance with just a few seats, a table and a large crucifix. The friar motioned for Tazio to sit down, promising a drop of a liqueur which was a local speciality and considered a sort of divine nectar.

The simplicity, the smell of beeswax and wood, and the courtesy of the friar conveyed first silence and then calm. 'It doesn't matter,' Tazio said to himself, 'it doesn't matter at all. Here you really are outside the world and it is actually better to say nothing.' Yet faced with a glass of liqueur in front of him, and the jovial look from his host, he could not resist the temptation to explain himself and to justify why he raced.

'We are like explorers,' Tazio started to say with no trace of malice in his voice. 'We are experimenting with new machinery, with modern solutions, and applying them to the cars which we then put to the test. But it is not just this, my dear friar, it is also the thrill of driving, of being able to race and compete. It is a kind of recital, where instead of Shakespeare, instead of talking, we interpret space and time. We accelerate. Is there anything more modern? We want to advance in every sense, and this is what the people want. They love watching our challenges, and they love to discuss them afterwards.'

In that rather austere room, with the friar sitting silently opposite him, Tazio continued to talk about himself and his world. He spoke of his passion for speed and for motor cars. He reminisced about the time on a motorbike in the Tourist Trophy where he cornered so close to a wall that a piece of finger was shaved off and he continued of course because it is just too exhilarating to race. It is just so exhilarating, seeing things squeezed into a blur, sliding past at the side of the road in escape from the world as you know it. He talked of how he felt inside when that growling of engines seizes you before the start of a race, biting your soul, almost making you sick with the desire to finish ahead of everyone else.

'Just think, Father, I've cracked loads of bones in my time,' he went on. 'They've had to put me in plaster but, even wrapped up like an Egyptian mummy, I was in the saddle to race, because being away from it, I get this crazy feeling which won't let me have any peace.'

Sitting in the centre of the bare room, opposite a crucifix, Nuvolari took an imaginary steering wheel in his hand and showed the Friar how to drive an Alfa 1750. He showed him his personal technique, that distinctive method for sliding the car through a bend. Tazio described the way in which he would point the nose of the car at the inside of the curve, with a skill no other driver was capable of. The others would have braked much sooner, while he did not touch the brake as the car slid sideways in a sudden movement, keeping the accelerator to the floor all the while. This was his method for taking a bend, to dice with the clutch and steering wheel, trying to keep the car on the road so it was tamed and controlled and in the correct position at the start of the straight, ready to pick up speed.

Tazio talked and talked, explaining his every move to the friar, so much so that he was unaware he had been talking for an interminable length of time, seated opposite the other man who listened so patiently. He could see himself in the cockpit, full of excitement, with one hand above an imaginary gear stick, the other pointing ahead explaining how to overtake a phantom Varzi, and he suddenly felt a little ashamed. Lowering his voice he said:

'I'm really sorry for going on so much, I expect you've loads to do. I've wasted a lot of your time. I just wanted to explain.'

Smiling, the friar stood up and said:

'It doesn't matter at all. Listening to people is my job. You race, I stay still. Everyone has their role to play, even the rain you will have noticed has made you talk. It's late now, signor Nuvolari, and the rain has stopped. I'll show you the road you need to take.'

Feeling rather embarrassed Tazio followed the friar to the door. When he noticed that the sky had dried up and the red Alfa was there waiting for him, he felt as though everything had returned to how it was before. He returned to the car in a happier mood and with a great bound he was behind the steering wheel again.

'This vehicle is like your lady,' the friar said to Tazio with a smile as he looked carefully at the Alfa. 'It really is beautiful and elegant. I can now understand how you could become so involved in the sport.'

Then raising his voice above the noise of the moving pistons he said, 'Don't forget the sky above. Remember the clouds, think of the storms.' The friar waved his hand in a gesture of farewell as Tazio had already begun to accelerate away.

Many years later in another Mille Miglia, Nuvolari again found himself in a rainstorm. It was '48, and he was a legend by this time, belting towards Reggio with a huge advantage over the car in second place. As ever, people hailed him from the side of the road, admiring the determination and courage shown by the little man. For those watching from the kerb at the edge of the road, he really seemed like a flash of red lightning, fleeting and ferocious, shooting across the asphalt as quick as an intake of breath. Tazio drove on because he knew he must, but a heavy burden weighed upon him. He was fifty-seven years old, and the Alfa team had released him to take on the much younger Varzi, so he had been forced to seek his fortune in Germany. He had driven the silver Auto Union to triumphs, but the burden had continued to torment him. Two of his children had died, one after the other, and now his own lungs had started to bleed, perhaps because of the gases discharged from the exhaust pipe which he had breathed in, or perhaps because his soul was escaping from within and he was starting to feel a sense of desperation. In Milan he had raced in the Gran Premio del Parco with one hand on the steering wheel. The other kept a handkerchief to his mouth to stem the flow of blood from his lungs.

This Mille Miglia that he was dominating seemed a small victory in the worst circumstances. Winning as a youngster was to be expected. Anyone can be a hero when their powers are fresh, their bones are intact and life is ahead of them. Yet when you have overtaken the whole world, everything slows up all of a sudden and you freeze inside as you struggle to make sense of things. To win in such circumstances is something that no-one can understand and no-one can explain.

Driving a Cisalfa the year before, Nuvolari had found himself close to the finish line when the car came to a standstill caused by a stupid loose connection and flash of sparks; a tiny problem, but one which had robbed him of victory and of one of the remaining drops of his lifeblood.

On that day in 1948 the sky again played games with the champion. He had been told that he was first at Reggio by a long way, but now the rain had worked its way inside the car's engine making it sneeze in fits and starts, forcing the driver to stop. In the midst of the storm, his eyes clouded with the frustration of another defeat, another slap in the face. Tazio looked around in desperation and he felt himself relive an old dream, a sort of unfinished nightmare. He was conscious that he had passed that way many years before, before everything had happened. So he stepped out of the car to ascertain where he was.

The doorway was made of solid wood just as he remembered it, and he noticed the entrance hall where he had taken refuge from a different storm. It felt natural for Tazio to bang on the door and wait for the same voice from long ago to respond. After a few hard knocks on the wood, Nuvolari heard someone within ask who it was that wanted help.

'It's me, Tazio Nuvolari the racing driver. I'm looking for a bit of shelter,' he almost shouted, as if only a few minutes rather than several years had passed.

The same familiar face appeared at the door; the same beard; the same cheerful open smile followed by a quick glance at the heavens.

'I see you wait for a storm before you come to see us,' said the friar, throwing open the door. He motioned to Tazio to come in and embraced him like a long-lost friend. It seemed as though nothing had changed in the time since their first meeting when Nuvolari had taken shelter from the rain. There were the same steps, the same sounds, the same cloister. There was the same austere room with only a few seats and the large crucifix. Once again the two men sat down opposite each other. Perhaps the repetition of his actions acted as a catalyst, or it was simply a stage in the passage of his life, because in the silence of that room Tazio Nuvolari felt the burden which had weighed in his chest start to move itself and slip away. Sitting opposite the friar, opposite time that had stood still, perhaps he saw himself many years earlier taken with the desire to explain his world and where he wanted to go; to discuss the miles he had already covered and those which still lay ahead. Everything seemed to become condensed in that instant, everything seemed to be immediate, and on his dust-covered face there seemed to appear kilometres of tears and a racing engine which sobbed in silence.

The friar moved over to him, and as the champion made a gesture to say something, he said:

'Don't say a word. It doesn't matter, I understand. You have covered many miles and you can't turn back. Racing is no easy matter, especially if now you cannot really race but only escape from the burden of life and those people who watch you from the edge of the road. They incite you, reminisce about you. You make these people dream. They call you Nuvola, and they admire you from the ground, watching you fly, performing legendary feats, heavenly things.'

Then he handed the champion a handkerchief and while Tazio dried his tears he added:

'In fact, this is really your storm.'

Nuvolari stood up and embraced the friar again, before following him out without a word. He waved goodbye from the doorway, but it was only when he reached his car that he was able to smile at the friar and say:

'Thank you. Perhaps it is like you say. Getting caught in the rain was meant to happen. But rain and water have their courses marked out for them. Water falls, then flows and ends up in the sea. I have competed against everything and everyone. I've covered all the roads in the world and I still don't know where I'll end up.'

After this encounter, Nuvolari continued to compete in a few more races until the final one, the Palermo–Monte Pellegrino, which naturally he won. He was fifty-eight years old and had just three more years to live. Who knows what sort of life he would have had if he had remained stationary, without motor racing.

Tazio Nuvolari died in his bed in Mantua, the day after a large storm.

Endurance

Emil Zatopek left his house early on the morning of 27 June 1968. He set off running towards the suburbs, ready to eat up the kilometres of his training route. Even though he had stopped competing some years before, he had never given up this part of his daily routine. With his head leaning to one side and his mouth twisted in a pained expression, every day he repeated this rite which had fascinated him since him he was a small child. It was not just running, it was toil. Twenty seven years ago at Zlin, just after his debut race had finished, he swore he would never compete again. It wasn't worth it. He had finished after one thousand four hundred metres of pain; an eternity spent searching for breath and any remaining strength, just to come second. On the podium, with the notes of the band in the air, the chief of the delegation had shaken his hand, complimented him on his performance and predicted that he had a great future ahead of him. The man was plump and hearty, probably a grocer, and was keenly involved in his important duties. To hide his embarrassment, Zatopek assumed a polite and serious manner; he thanked him and reassured him that he would give everything and run with determination. As a prize, the man offered him a gold-plated fountain pen.

Returning to Koprivnice some hours later, gently rocked by the movement of the train, the boy fell asleep in the warm carriage and dreamt of being out training. He was running along a railway line, harnessed like a horse to a steam train which remained cool and calm, leaving Zatopek to pull hard. He ran and pulled as if he was Hercules or Atlantis, sweating and suffering until he had eaten up the kilometres to his wife Dana, and his parents in Koprivnice. The people shouted for joy and thanked him as they climbed down from the train. When the train came to a stop with a jolt it really appeared to be at a station, but the platform was deserted and everything had disappeared except for his fatigue. Anxiously he climbed out of the carriage and went home in a flash.

Since then he had never stopped running. He flew. He had devised a special method of training: running in a field for four-hundred metres fifteen times and, the day after, running twenty two-hundred-metre sprints like the wind, come rain or shine. He would even wear heavy military boots to test himself under the most exacting conditions, so that when it was time to race he would find it a kind of relief. As a result of this punishing schedule, this drawn-out suffering, an ugly grimace became imprinted on his face, the mark of real pain. To those who commented on this look, or his cart-horse running style that lacked any trace of elegance, the champion would always make the same reply:

'It doesn't matter. You can see I can't manage both things at once. I don't have enough talent to run and smile at the same time.'

On that June morning he was already a legendary figure, a hero for the people of Bohemia. He had won at the Olympics, the European Championships and had set world record times. In thirty-eight races between 1948 and 1954 no one had been able to overtake him, allowing him to achieve extraordinary feats. At the Helsinki Olympics he had won the five- and ten-thousand metre events. The marathon remained, and he wanted to make an attempt to conquer it. Never before had a man won all these events together, no one had ever really tried. The marathon is not just a race about stamina, it is a descent into the soul; it is about courage, tactics and exhaustion. It requires special knowledge and dedication, so it is run only by specialists. As it was the first time Zatopek had made such an attempt, he found himself in new territory at the start. In addition, his legs already held other victories over other distances, but he had the determination and hope that his training could help him in this undertaking. He had the humility of the great so, instead of any rash conduct at the start, he positioned himself behind the heels of the Englishman Peters, who was the current champion and favourite for the race.

As the race began, Zatopek tried to run with the regular tempo set

78

by the marathon runners, but he found it difficult and had to work hard to keep up with them. After fifteen kilometres he had caught up and he took a look at the group. He felt like a fish out of water, a novice. Perhaps he felt afraid for having embarked on an adventure that was too much for him. A debutant thrust into a murderous race without knowing the right moments to dance away. Endurance running is similar to the movement of music, to the ticking of a watch. You need to make and remake the same action, that forward leaning motion with just the right stimulus, a precise cadence so that the mainspring does not snap or you do not consume all your energy before precisely the right moment has arrived. So he innocently came up next to Jim Peters, who led the race, and breathing hard asked in simple English if they were running at a good pace or whether it was too fast or too slow.

'Excuse me,' he said, 'but this is my first time you know.'

The other man was feeling the pressure (he would later admit that the tempo was already very high) and was annoyed by the unusual question. Maybe in the hope of giving the Czech a low blow he said that yes, the tempo was too slow, and that with such a light rhythm they would never get to the finish. So the new marathon runner, worried now, replied with heartfelt thanks and picked up his pace, dropping the competitors and arriving first at the stadium where thousands of excited Finns were on their feet waiting to greet him.

Now, many years later, Zatopek trained the sports team of the regiment of which he was colonel, making use of his prestige and the wealth of experience from running against everybody and always being the winner. Watching him run through the streets of Prague each morning, with that particular cadence and that grimace, people recognised the champion's style and they would wave and clap their hands in appreciation. Zatopek was much loved for his political work and for his honesty. On the evening of 27 June, that we are discussing here, he had just signed the 'Dubcek Manifesto', two-thousand words calling for dignity and independence.

'We have the right to govern ourselves without being held on a leash,' the hero colonel said as he signed, 'for the socialism we believe in.'

Running through Prague on that early morning, pounding his feet on the half-deserted streets, he felt the tepid air on his face, the spring air which seemed to bring with it something new. His proverbial grimace softened a little, becoming almost a smile. He heard his steps being doubled, their echo falling more heavily and next to him appeared the panting face of someone he thought he knew. The man in a tracksuit motioned to him and said:

'Good morning comrade Zatopek. Allow me to take a stretch of road with you. The air is sweet this morning. Prague looks amazing. I'll have the pleasure of running in the shadow of a champion, a national hero, our national pride.'

Zatopek gave a nod of assent. He tended not to say much, as in races and training he was accompanied by his thoughts. Nonetheless he smiled faintly, pretending to look pleased because he was grateful to the people who loved and respected him for committing himself to a life of exhaustion. So he just gave a nod, an invitation to run, given with a good heart and courtesy. Despite his heavy breathing the man started to speak, first praising the champion and then shortly afterwards slipping into the political situation.

'It's a pity that a man like you,' he said, 'wants to get involved in things which are rather murky. Hasn't the habit of pushing your body, of running in the lead under pressure made you consider that you are a colonel in the army, that you are an obedient military man who has to uphold strict responsibilities? You may find yourself running on the wrong track, and that could be bad for your health.'

The man's voice was broken by the rhythm of his running stride, but it still had a precise timbre, the hard tone of someone who knew how to drive home a point. And as the man spoke it seemed to Zatopek that he really did recognise his face, the face of a military colleague. The message was very clear, direct advice to stop his recent political work. In Zatopek's stomach rose a deep feeling of intolerance that troubled the champion enough to increase his tempo a little and leave that voice behind, panting clumsily, taking him away from the warning but not from the anger which was just beginning. That evening he went to sign the spring manifesto and used sharp words regarding the dignity of mankind. As he uttered them he looked around for one particular face, fiercely scanning, without losing his rhythm whatsoever.

Later that summer, on the morning of 13 August, Prague was awash with rumours that Russian tanks were about to intervene to preserve the political alliance. It was a rude awakening, reality thrown in the face, an armed reality that upset the springtime and cracked the summer leaving the people and the city feeling frozen. Zatopek did not listen to the entreaties of his wife Dana. He did not listen to reason, he said that he had to adhere to his training programme and left the house as if nothing was going on. He plunged into the icy streets and ran along Mala Strana, arriving in the ancient part of the city that by now was under occupation, with desperate people crying, shouting and grappling with the tanks. He ran for the whole morning, his stride dragging in a way it never had before, his characteristic grimace swollen almost to bursting point.

That evening he was called to report to Headquarters, he a high ranking military man, to give justification for signing an illegal document in support of a revolution. The building he was called to was tall and grey with a dark entrance hall and Zatopek felt for a moment like K inside the castle[1]. It wasn't so different he thought, just three buildings, a bit higher. It dominated the golden city that now appeared to him bronze and grey, a city where the life of a boy went up in a puff of smoke after he had set himself on fire in an attempt for freedom[2].

After Zatopek was made to wait for hours, an act of intimidation, he was led into a room and took a seat. The tone of voice he heard was dry but still holding respect for someone important. It is hard to forget a symbol in an instant, especially if they have represented the people, if they have made them dream. From the other part of the room a person he recognised was waiting for him. It was the runner from that unfortunate morning when he had been warned that the spring would quickly evaporate.

1 A reference to Franz Kafka's novel, *The Castle*.
2 A history student named Jan Palach set himself on fire on 16 January 1969 in protest against the Soviet-led invasion of Czechoslovakia.

'Comrade Zatopek,' the man said to him, 'I'm sorry. I had warned you, but you really run too much. That morning you ran off and you didn't let me finish. Now you are forced to listen to me, but about things which have happened, and it seems to me they are things that are not very pretty. You are a hero, a symbol. You are an image that it will do no good to stain. Follow my advice: retract. You have made a mistake, there has been a misunderstanding. You have run, so to speak, in haste. You have gone too far ahead and now you are able to consider that it is better to wait and catch your breath. Sign here and then go home. Tomorrow you return to the barracks and the training ground. Life can carry on in peace. After spring comes summer. Then autumn and winter will arrive. Just sign.'

So saying he held out a typed piece of paper, that Zatopek refused even to glance at.

'It doesn't matter,' he said. 'I've never had a peaceful life comrade, don't worry. And I've never run too much or too hard. In fact I think I still have much to learn. Training methods, work to carry out, programmes and responsibilities. Above all I must perfect my endurance which is my great strength. Remember when I beat the world in eight days, doing the five-thousand, ten-thousand and marathon? Perhaps it's possible to do better, to endure a bit more. It's worth trying.'

'You should think about it yourself,' said Zatopek as he was about to leave. 'When you run your breathing is broken and you puff and wheeze. Listen to what I say to you: your voice is steady only when you are sitting down, when you are comfortable in the warmth of a room. Like that it is easy, anyone can do it. It doesn't seem any great effort to me.'

Zatopek was suspended from his work in the military sports department and a few days later was expelled from the party. Normality was triumphing and he was by now no longer considered normal. He was just a wild horse who ran in too much of a hurry; a human locomotive who only knew how to pull hard. He was called once again to that grey building to receive an official letter which stripped him of his rank and responsibilities as well as the opportunity to continue his coaching. He found other work. He, the people's hero, set himself to being a builder, putting up brick walls on the houses of the people for whom he had competed.

Prague was getting colder and darker, and although he did not feel afraid it was with some difficulty that the champion held back the wish to escape. Many friends from abroad, enthusiasts and sportsmen, had offered him golden bridges to help him emigrate. While pondering over bricks and races Zatopek really refined his endurance, his ability to live with the impulse to escape always close at hand.

In the pitch black of a February morning, Zatopek left early as usual on his training run. The weather was dark and so was his mood as he mused on his life with each step.

'A man is a man,' he said to himself. 'He is weak and has clearly defined limits. How can I continue to ask myself and those who are dear to me to tolerate this situation, the destruction of dignity and this bullying? There seems no end to this descent which is hammering my character and my work. Such destructive things can make you ill. The step towards a respectable life is a short one. A ticket, a telephone call, to accept something that has already been prepared, followed by a peaceful life in exile.'

As he ran in the cold the champion's head was filled with these thoughts perhaps in search of a solution, when he noticed that someone else was running at his side. For a moment he again saw the scene of months earlier, and he felt a sense of annoyance, believing that it was the face of the man who had threatened him. Instead it was a lad wrapped up in a large jersey, his head almost covered by a scarf. He was tall and he moved with a light step.

'Mr Zatopek,' he said, 'please continue your race, continue to perfect your endurance. We are all grateful for your presence, for the fact that you have not left Prague, that you are here alone battling on. Think of what I say: we are already on the run, we have sprung away and they have recaptured us. It is from you that we have learned not to be defeated, to never give up. To grit the teeth even when you feel pain, even if it seems the weight of the world is on your shoulders. It is from you that we have learned not to have fear, that if we look ugly when we are running, if we are sweating or have cramp, the important thing to remember is that we are running to reach the finish. You have taught us the power of stamina, to try each day to increase it by a metre. We need you because the escape will be a long one, and to think that a human locomotive is running with us will give us hope and strength to continue with our race. The armed forces have taken away your job, but you continue to keep training.'

Zatopek wanted to respond, to say that he was just a man, that what he had done was nothing heroic, just run and try. He wanted to say that it wasn't anything that could be of use in supporting the enormous weight of the leash that the people wore, but he did not have time to open his mouth because the boy quickly raised his tempo and shot ahead, disappearing into the dark in a few seconds. Before he vanished like a ghost, as he ran he turned towards the champion, and under the faint light of a street lamp his movement caused the scarf to slip revealing a face which was disfigured, on fire and almost burnt. It was only a moment, not even an instant, before everything disappeared except for the street, the cold and the sense that the face glimpsed like lightning was a dream, a mirage. Perhaps it was a dark thought to have associated his own difficulties to a lad whose courage had made him set fire to himself.

Soon afterwards, Zatopek was again called to the same building. Again he was made to wait for hours and was finally admitted to the same room where the functionary seemed to have a relaxed air.

'My dear comrade,' he said, 'as you can see we have not forgotten you. You understand that you cannot stay in the armed forces, apart from the fact that you now have a good job as a builder and can make yourself useful constructing houses, buildings and schools. However we believe that really you are wasted, you are actually trained for toil and you have demonstrated great stamina in your performances. Moreover, you said to me that you always want to do better, and so we have thought at length about how to make best use of the gifts which have made you famous. There is a uranium mine in the north where strong arms are needed to haul the carts from the bottom of the earth. It seems that this work is suited to your needs. It is our role to meet the wishes of a hero and give you a way to train your legendary endurance.'

The champion gave a half smile, almost a grimace.

'Thank you,' he said, 'it was just what I was looking for. You will not believe that once I dreamt I was a locomotive, pulling the carriages dragging and sweating. You really need to know what are your own limits, how to change your stride and rhythm, when to increase your level of force. And running in different parts of the world, challenging people accustomed to competition, I have come to learn that there is a big difference between running and escaping. So I'll go calmly to the mine and push the uranium carts for as long as I can. Patience is all you can have, whether you have a grimace on your face or not, because being perfect is not the important thing. The important thing is to make sure you understand.'

In the fading daylight, Zatopek quickly left the building. He moved towards the darkness feeling years of fatigue and suffering as if he was a condemned man. The sun's reflection illuminated Prague in gold as the city watched him run towards his home with the usual grimace of pain and his usual heavy step; that step which was still firm and enduring.

The Englishman
and il Bersagliere[1]

At dawn on 4 July 1865, with his fists fixed to the sides of his bed, Jean-Antoine Carrel woke suddenly after a dream in which he had been thrown down a mountainside. Feeling a sense of liberation from the summit of the Matterhorn he had seen the familiar profile of the mountains and valleys below defined like the lines on a hand. Deep within he had tasted the curious flavour of the knowledge that he was the first person to do something strangely important; of being the first person capable of climbing the distance which divides us from ourselves and yet does not quite give us peace. In descending from the summit the satisfaction had vanished as a sense of guilt took over, guilt for having confronted the mountain and for having violated it. He had managed to touch the myth, and conquering that summit had smashed any doubt that scaling the mystery was something only to be dreamt of, as you try to live in hope, without really knowing exactly what to do.

During his descent in the dream, perhaps weighed down by these thoughts, the rope which joined him to his companions became stretched out. It was now no more than a fine thread, unsuitable for its job, so worn that the last pull gave a snap which caused it to break. Carrel fell, spinning head over heels in the ravine, falling away metre after metre until he found himself clinging to the sides of his bed.

From high above the world in his dream, he looked in the direction of Zermatt and could just make out some tiny figures who were attempting the climb from the other side.

'It's that presumptuous Englishman,' thought Carrel, 'that Whymper who thinks he's the best and tries to climb mountains by

1 an armed hunter or sharpshooter

exploring new routes. We were actually born here under the Matterhorn. We are its children and we give it respect. From our homes below we look at it as you would look at a father who is strict but gentle also. It is a sculpture of power and beauty, but also one of sweat, cold and hard work. Climbing to the top of the world is not a preoccupation for us, because we think of how to survive before anything else, something that is not always certain in these valleys. But if someone wants to go to the top, or someone wants to discover new horizons, then it is right that one of us should have a go. That person should be the best, so it should be Jean Antoine Carrel, known as *il Bersagliere*.'

Carrel prepared his bags as he thought, and waited for his companions to be ready. Alpine climbing in those days was quite primitive and a large undertaking without today's technologically developed equipment. A few pickaxes, hard shoes, thick woollen jerseys and a few sticks to lean on and keep your balance. There were the first climbing ropes made from hemp that became saturated in snow and ice, eventually turning dry and brittle like glass or marble. The guides looked at the equipment with diffidence as though it was some sort of strange fashion which the Englishmen also carried, along with their mania for climbing to the summit while tied together like salami. Their bodies and destinies were tied together in case some of the support had been badly made. Carrel preferred to use the strength and patience of a step taken with methodical care; one step after another, crawling up the mountain, looking well ahead without overdoing it. You were joined to no one and to no thing. You alone were the master of your experience built from years of silent waiting.

He would have preferred to go alone, challenging himself from within, with only himself to find the right solution to the conundrum of a climb. He had attempted it on at least seven other occasions, edging closer to the Matterhorn with great care; watching; making his eyes and feet understand the route. He had even discouraged the Englishman among others who had wanted to make an attempt.

'Why do you want to go up there?' he once said to Whymper. 'Leave it alone, choose a more docile mountain than this pyramid to which stone and snow cling. It is a mysterious mountain that you cannot underestimate. Every time you make an attempt it makes an excuse: there is a storm, a landslide, a sudden shower that soaks the rocks like rags. And then there is the legend which is handed down in the valley from father to son. It's about evil spirits; a bewitched mountain that requires a human sacrifice in order to be conquered – a price too high to pay.'

Whymper had mumbled something in his strange tongue and, taking his hat, had retired to his hotel to consider the best way organise his attempt. He would wait for the right moment to test whether the mountain really would refuse an Englishman the pleasure of getting to know it.

'Perhaps it was just a matter of politeness,' he thought, 'of your point of view. I am an explorer, a naturalist, an author and photographer. I will climb that mountain and tell everyone how the world is made. I know how to get to the top and look around.'

During those July days in Breuil, Carrel knew that the Englishman had not given up but was waiting for the right moment. So he quickly decided to be ready to start the climb on the morning of the 14th. The party was well put together, comprising his brother Cesar and another guide, the great mountaineer Jean Joseph Maquignaz and the abbot Carlo Gorret, who was an important figure in Valsavarenche. According to the plans, they would attack the Matterhorn to reach victory, the fruit of the hopes, sacrifices, projects and attempts made by il Bersagliere. They would arrive before the others, bringing glory to the valley rather than to an island far away that could not even claim a hill of any significance.

The men from the valley left for the attack convinced that this was a good opportunity. The timing was perfect. The weather was dry and calm for a quick, trouble-free ascent. Apart from their pickaxes and rope they carried with them large flasks attached to their knapsacks which contained the only true remedy for fatigue. It was not today's simpamine or some sort of diabolical concoction, but simply a life-giving water made from good grappa to warm the legs, to extract every ounce of strength, a panacea for all ills. So they departed, certain to give their utmost to the climb, and finally bring some reward to the years of exploration spent by Carrel. The climb from Breuil was by now more or less mapped out. Only the last part was missing; the last leap of a few hundred metres to seal another moment in history.

Whymper seethed in his hotel room, angrily turning over in his mind the lack of a group who could help him make the ascent. He knew that il Bersagliere was ready to go and that his next attempt was imminent. He spent hours alone in torment, unable to do anything, as the Matterhorn stood before him defiantly. All of a sudden there was a hubbub in the entrance hall of the hotel as a group of people rang the bell for service. Just back from the Teodulo refuge, they included Lord Francis Douglas, a great climber and one of the youngest members of the Alpine Club. With him was the older Peter Taugwalder, with whom had climbed the Wellenkuppe. The hotel guests gathered around them and listened to their tales of the adventure. His Lordship talked and explained, describing how he made the climb, giving a satisfied laugh with the enjoyment of retelling the story. In a second Whymper gave a start and let out a deep breath. Why not strike while the iron was hot? He knew the ambition of Lord Douglas. Taugwalder too seemed an ideal companion. So he barged his way into the group with polite apologies, and almost shouting at Lord Douglas took him aside as the rest of the group looked on with surprise. Over a warming cup of grog and with a trembling voice he outlined the situation he was in, explaining that Carrel would soon be on the move, that the climb would soon be done. If that were to be the case then the man from the valley would take all the glory of the exploration, while the Matterhorn would remain at the window, beaten only by the tenacity of the rough Bersagliere.

Whymper talked and talked obsessively in a very excited state. He would have to convince Douglas about everything, perhaps even persuading him to join forces with the devil himself.

'We are going from the other part of Zermatt. We will take Taugwalder and we will approach in a wide loop,' he said. 'At least there will be someone else to have a try to compete with Carrel's route towards the Matterhorn.'

The words were left suspended in the air. For a moment or two life itself remained immobile. In that time his companion finished the hot liquor then looked him in the eye and, from deep within himself, finally said, 'Of course I'll accept.' Then he made a nod to say it was time to go.

So in a hurry they would go back, passing by Teodulo once more, to the other part of Zermatt. On entering the hotel they came across Michel Croz, a guide from Savoy currently teamed with Charles Hudson. Whymper asked to meet Hudson who gave his consent to allow Croz to take part in the climb on the condition that he too could come, along with a young climber named Roger Hadow who had recently arrived from Mont Blanc.

The trip was becoming complicated, the climbing party too large. Whymper made an irritated gesture with his hand. Time was pressing however, and with the inclusion of Croz, the climb had every chance of success. On this they were all agreed, so on the evening of 13 July the company, together with one of Taugwalder's sons, left together. They would set up camp so that the following morning they could finally make their attack on the mountain.

Following a strange sort of destiny, both parties found themselves asleep under the Matterhorn on the same night but on opposite sides of the mountain. Both parties had the same aim, the same hopes divided by the giant rock. Carrel as we have said dreamt of the climb and after having reached the summit saw himself fall, under the weight of an unexplained sense of guilt.

In his own dream Whymper saw the same scene but he saw it from a different perspective. He saw Carrel point at him from the summit, and together with Gorret they shouted down to him. He was forced to turn back as he heard hurrahs of joy from above. With a heavy heart and a feeling of anguish he returned to Zermatt to wait.

In their camp under the bulk of the mountain a sticky veil spread itself out, a dense slumber which would lead to a slow waking, a waking made heavy with the sensation of a challenge too difficult to undertake. Without a word, without a gesture, Whymper's group readied themselves for the climb. The Matterhorn was already too high and the hour was now very late.

With the morning light il Bersagliere and his team left earlier than the others. The conditions seemed ideal. The sky was calm and clear. With a good step the summit would gradually get lower. Carrel led the way with the confidence of someone who knew the rocks well. With a steady rhythm he quickly covered the distance already calculated in his plans. Every hour they took a break to catch their breath and take eat some food; a piece of bread, a drop or two of honey and some grappa to warm the chest. It was during one of these breaks that Abbot Gorret started to talk. As though certain of a successful outcome he said that he would write a memorial which would inform the whole world about the climb. Not just as a report, but a consideration of the human condition on a journey which took seemingly insane routes towards a much-longed-for objective. He would take the search for knowledge, the necessity of knowing into account. He would consider scientific realities and the demands they made, along with the beauty of creation.

On the journey towards the top, the words of the abbot insinuated themselves into the group, accompanying them on their perfect climb, in harmony with mankind, God and the universe. But il Bersagliere was a man of few words. Yes, mountains for him were beautiful, but they also represented a struggle, something silent which beat within the chest, within your heart made from toil. Perhaps it was at this point that he started to feel lost. He was not a man of many words, but a man made of silences and of mountains which coursed in his blood. Those opinions, which were now climbing with the party, seemed to him almost profane. It was as if the need to explain and give meaning to why you put one leg in front of another as you crawled up the mountain was too heavy a load to carry. So at the next break for recuperation, with a big effort, he warned them not to take it all too seriously, adding his objection that perhaps climbing to the summit was a sin. All this he said in one breath as the grappa choked in his chest.

The time was now well advanced and the sun bore down on the granite, melting the snow and unsettling the rocks. The prudent approach was to put your head down and press on before night fell on the mountain, throwing no more wood on the fire of the discussion. There is no precise form to the way things happen. Instead things happen and then wait for us to give them some order. Time passes for explanations and obscure reasonings which follow no set route, but are really like mountains to be scaled. For many years Abbot Gorret would have to think how this absurd situation arose, and how little by little the conversation became a mixture, a kind of glue which lost them time and reason. In old age, in a diary that explained very little, he had penned a mysterious phrase in French where he spoke of personality, of real love, of something about which sooner or later he would have to talk. It was something linked to pride he had never spoken about, of his irritation with Carrel who had stopped himself only a few steps from the summit and looked at the top with something like regret. Perhaps it was the level of fatigue which by now must have been huge. Perhaps it was a mist from the grappa that caused confusion. Instead of spurring his team on to attack, to gather up their last reserves of energy, il Bersagliere stared at the summit transfixed, asking his companions if perhaps their desire was committing a sin.

'Are we sure of our actions,' he asked, 'that in arriving up there we are not ruining something that I know myself I have always searched for? Where can we go after the summit? Think about it, which mountain is left when all of them have been scaled?'

While this conversation was taking place, on the other side Whymper was climbing swiftly. Everything was going too easily, without the hitches or dramas that so often accompany large endeavours. His only real hindrance came not from the rocks or the difficulty of the mountain, but from his obsession with being preceded by the Italians who were arriving at the summit. With one foot in front of the other, climbing hurriedly, Whymper felt that he was just a step away from victory, although a wave of fear swept over him. The dream he had experienced where Carrel waved to him gave his mouth the taste of defeat. The Englishman was a man of great determination who wanted to complete his challenge whatever the cost. He wanted his name to be forever associated with one route, one summit, one climb. Even in photographs or wood cuts, he was careful to include a mountain in the background as if to illustrate his own mission, his own destiny. You would see his worried face, his brow furrowed, his square jaw. His eyes had the look of one who is almost hallucinating, the eyes of a young animal searching for his own soul on the mountains.

So the Matterhorn had to be his, that much was clear, and today the mountain was giving its endorsement to his attempt. The climb went smoothly without any obstacles, and after an hour and forty minutes Whymper had reached the summit. In his throat he held a strangled shout together with the fear that after ascending the last wall of rock he would see Carrel already there, laughing at him. After gaining the last easy rocks he untied himself from the rope and scrambled towards the very top where there was absolutely nothing to be seen except for a carpet of soft snow on the stones. Whymper turned and looked around, anxiously looking for some sign, some trace. Then he turned towards Croz who was just arriving and he gave a shout of victory throwing wide his arms. He had sealed a place in history; he was the first to conquer both the Matterhorn and the nightmare which had assailed him.

Leaning over to the Italian side from the crest they could see Carrel climbing with three companions far down below.

'*Ah les coquins,*' said Croz with a laugh. '*Ils sont bien en bas.*'

In an exact opposite of Whymper's dream they started to shout hurrahs and threw small stones to make themselves heard. Then they waved their arms in the hope that il Bersagliere would notice them.

Hearing the noise of the stones the four Italians stopped on a ridge. With the echo of the calls a sudden chill stopped their movement. Only Carrel with a serious face looked down. He barely had the voice to say:

'Those are the spirits of the mountain. Can you hear them? It would be useless for us to continue any further.'

No one had the courage to object. So they turned their backs to the mountain, and by late evening had returned to the valley.

Whymper's pride had triumphed. In his diaries he wrote: 'On the summit of the Matterhorn I spent an intense hour of marvellous vitality.' He also made a sketch, and seemed drunk with the satisfaction and glory. He imagined he would become a legendary figure, unaware that actually life is not always in our own hands. The climb was over but the adventure was unfinished. The group prepared for their descent, and in the general contentedness joined themselves together without too much thought. They had linked themselves carelessly with an old rope unable to offer any real security. The guide then took the rope, tied a knot and the party's descent began. Leading the way was the expert Croz, then Hadow, Hudson, Douglas and the older Taugwalder, while Whymper with his sketch still in his hand hurriedly took hold of the rope as the first men were already onto the steep slope. He looped the rope round his waist, then threw the end to the younger Taugwalder who grabbed it to form the end of the line.

From the first few moments of the descent young Hadow showed signs of fatigue. Only nineteen years old, he had been up Mont Blanc a few days earlier in a record-breaking time. Perhaps it was the emotion of the climb they had just completed, perhaps he was exhausted, apart from the fact that the soles of his climbing shoes had worn out. Croz in the lead had a hard job to keep his footing secure with each step taken, often forced to put his stick on the ground thus leaving himself with nothing to lean on for balance. As the guide worked to find a good grip, Hadow slipped and flew down into Croz, hitting him on the back. There was a succession of desperate shouts as Hudson then Douglas were torn away. It had happened in an instant which, on the mountain, seemed eternal. Shouts burst into the air, hands grabbed at thin air and in a sudden break in the noise the shock of the broken rope between Lord Douglas and Taugwalder was felt. Whymper clung to the rock and turned in time to see his four companions falling in the void, hands frantically swirling as if they were trying to swim. They found the remains of three of them next day. Hadow with the threadbare soles of his shoes, the rope clearly cut and drenched in blood. There was no trace of the Lord who had been dispersed in the air then entombed in the rocks.

Whymper was accused of a lack of preparation, of not taking things seriously. They said he had thought too much about the glory of the achievement rather than of the most basic concern for mountaineers, safety. Someone accused him of having cut the cord to save himself, and this generated plenty of doubts and discussions. The accused Englishman defended himself from the onslaught and eventually returned to exploring. However he had forever given up the greatest climbs. Each evening when he found himself alone he felt the snap of the rope in the silence and he saw his four companions in free fall, swimming in mid air, loudly calling his name.

From Breuil, through his binoculars the engineer Giordano had seen someone moving about on the summit. He remembered il Bersagliere and his party, so he quickly telegraphed to the minister Sella: 'We have conquered the Matterhorn.' But Carrel returned dejected and humiliated. There was no real explanation for the defeat. Only Giordano, perhaps burning from embarrassment at his comical mistake, could encourage Carrel to make another attempt.

Il Bersagliere accepted and three days later he was at the summit. In Valtournenche after the triumph nobody knew of the death of the four men. From high on the mountain Carrel looked down and saw traces of the track disturbed within the ice; an old footprint. He remembered his dream and thought of the strange symmetry to what had happened, remembering how he had seen himself triumphant and looked down on a defeated Whymper below.

Carrel considered how strange life was, how the sense of things changes, how it can be hard to understand those things which we are obliged to do. In that moment the Matterhorn seemed to be no more than a rock to him.

Trusevich's Last Save

On 12 April 1942, in the courtyard of the bakery in Degtyarevskaya Street, Nikolai Trusevich found himself looking at the sky above Kiev. The sky was smeared in such a clear shade of white that it seemed like a trail of whipped cream. It will snow soon he thought as he leant against a wall to let the fatigue of his tough job flow from his body.

He turned his gaze towards the clouds, then shut his eyelids which were brushed by the icy wind. It was then that he noticed he was humming a blasphemous nursery rhyme to the tune of the dirge with which old Berberova had sung him to sleep when he was a child:

'Lord of the world, Lord of the sky, quickly send us the snow. Don't send a light veil, send a mountain, send a sea. Make it so that no-one can shoot any more. Send snow over Russia, Egypt and France. Send heaps like a plane unloading its deadly bombs over our houses. Make it so that your white stuff covers the earth, silencing noises, silencing war. Leave us to live in freshness, covered in snow. Far away from these Germans.'

He hoped he would fall asleep and wake up covered in white snow. So he further tightened his eyelids and rested his head against the cement wall while he continued to repeat the verses of his strange litany. He was so immersed in thought that he did not immediately notice that Josif Kordik was standing next to him. When he heard his voice he gave a start of surprise and also of embarrassment because he was sure the words he had been singing must have been heard.

'You don't need to pray, Nikolai,' said Kordik, 'the Germans won't be put off by a few flakes of snow. They've got shovels.'

For several months Ukraine had been overrun by the Nazis who had taken control of Kiev, governing it as conquerors. Normal life had ceased. As prisoners, the occupation had become a matter of survival. Each day was a case of trying to find a way of getting through to the evening, learning to do without the life that was slipping further away into the distance. Trusevich too had had to adapt. He was a great goalkeeper, a symbol of Dynamo Kiev, who had found a job in a bakery together with many of his fellow footballers.

'At least we don't feel too much hunger,' he said to those who felt the occupation did not take sporting glories into account. With his head low and his mouth drawn he made this comment with the shame of knowing that others were receiving much harsher treatment.

That evening, perhaps because of the melancholy words recited by his friend, or perhaps because of the mutual respect between the two men as they leant against the wall waiting for snow, an idea suddenly came to Josif Kordik, which he explained to the champion in a high voice like a hymn to counteract his sad prayer.

'Inside us Nikolai, we have enough raw material not to abandon ourselves to the life of a prisoner or slave,' said the baker with determination. 'I'm not talking about flour or bread. I'm talking about the best footballers the Ukraine has ever had. Apart from you there is Goncharenko, Sviridovskij, Korotkikh, Klimenko, Tyutchev, Putistin and Kuzmenko from Dynamo; Balakin, Sukharev and Melnik from Locomotive. Just think about it. There's a whole team there, of the best. Let's talk to the others and start playing again. We'll go outside this factory and challenge someone to a match. Kicking a football will make us find life again, showing the people of Kiev that we are not finished yet!'

This was how Start FC, were born: an unusual team, fused during wartime from the two biggest clubs in the city. Eleven captive footballers, eleven real stars, coached by an unlikely manager – a baker.

The courtyard of the large bakery in Degtyarevskaya Street became the training ground. Punishing routines watched by tormented eyes. They trained at night because the day was filled with working. Then they cleared the snow from the courtyard, forming mounds to be used as goalposts. The men felt tired and weak from their work and from their training, but the quality of play quickly returned to their legs and even the Germans made a few nods of appreciation and of admiration also.

Football has a strange magic, a universal language that is a feast for both body and mind, even in times of war. Even an enemy soldier can appreciate the perfect geometry of a well-organised move. One day the chief of the German guard, Krueger, called Kordik to his office near the main door. Sitting behind his desk, without giving any impression of conceding any confidence to the prisoner, he looked into the distance in the direction of a wall and said to the baker who stood opposite him:

'Your country is sad. The days in this part of the world are grey and dull even though summer is on the way. Our glorious troops need some outlet and Headquarters are looking for a challenge for the lorry drivers' team. I've noticed that you have been training a football team. They don't seem too bad. So you will play a match against us. The match will take place tomorrow.'

On 12 July 1942, Start made their debut. It was a humble opening on a small pitch behind the station against eleven rough lorry drivers with the stands almost exclusively filled with Germans. Before taking the field, Nikolai Trusevich looked up at the sky. The usual grey slate of cloud covered Kiev and its people including those in the hut being used as a dressing room. Nonetheless, wearing their match shirts and socks, Start were ready and it was clear that nothing could stop their will to be alive. Trusevich glanced at his team mates without uttering a word. In the centre of the pitch their play was life itself. They won the match 4–1 without over-exerting themselves, despite the crude challenges from the Germans and a referee who pretended to see nothing. Their prize for the victory was just a look. As he went to work the next day, Kordik's eyes met those of Krueger who held his gaze for an instant, before he changed direction and lowered his eyes without a breath. He felt as though he had won a trophy for Ukraine, and he felt himself to be a true champion.

Two days later he was once again asked to report to the office near the main door and, as though no match had ever been played, the German ordered Kordik to prepare his team for a meeting with the representatives of the engineers.

'For you who are little more than dogs this is a great honour,' he said adding coldly, 'Be ready, the match will be played tomorrow.'

On 17 July Start undertook their second challenge. They were unconscious of the fatigue of playing a match just five days after their first outing. They won 6-0. The engineers were taken to pieces despite playing with integrity. Halfway through the first half Goncharenko, out on the right, trapped the ball on the run, then he beat his marker with a lob before passing to the centre of the area for his teammate to score. As they hugged to celebrate the goal, amidst the clapping he noticed his opponent slowly move close to him and gaze at him in admiration, his mouth open as if he wanted to say something. Makar forgot that this was his enemy, seeing instead just a beaten man. He smiled towards his opponent who stayed immobile for a moment before turning on his heel. At the end of the match no German would offer his hand. That night Makar Goncharenko dreamt of a German stopping in his tracks to look at him in amazement as if he was looking at a Martian.

The first victories for Start had an effect. In that city crushed by hunger and death the victories of Start were like an embrace, a gesture of affection towards the people who carried out their lives in suffering. The Ukrainians talked a great deal about the last match, feeling themselves to be stronger and more contented. The great Dynamo team had returned under another name to give their enemies no end of trouble, and to give them a thread of hope.

On 19 July they took on MSG Wal, a Hungarian team of the highest level who played elegant football. They were full of invention, speed and aggression. The match finished with the same result, a triumph for the bakers. With great fluency they scored five times. At the end of the game, with the crowd singing for joy, Josif Kordik agreed to play a return match a week later.

MSG Wal gave everything to avoid losing face, to put on a show against players of a high standard. Start were thin, poorly trained and tired from forced work. The match was tough and hard fought. It was

Pavel Komarov who ensured the victory with a third goal after MSG had been ahead with two goals to one.

Seated in the grandstand, Major General Eberhardt had witnessed everything. Inside the stadium the Ukrainians celebrated their latest victory shouting with joy, their faces contented. They praised their players, the beloved Komarov and Goncharenko, as well as Trusevich who had made several saves. The Nazi gave a gesture of irritation. 'This subspecies,' he said, 'must be taught a lesson.'

At a meeting of the State Council, someone spoke of annihilation, of using a firm hand to wipe forever the satisfaction from the faces of the Ukrainians. It was Eberhardt in fact who searched for an answer.

'I don't believe that would be a judicious solution,' he said with a smile ironed onto his lips. 'Do you really think that killing someone, imprisoning someone else, will lessen the taste for these victories? And even if we did interrupt the exhibitions of their players, even if we forbade them to play, do you think their successes would be forgotten? Do you not believe that they would continue to be thought of as strong and invincible as they have been up till now?'

A silence fell on the room. Everyone understood what the Major General was saying. The sense of euphoria created by a decisive goal would not disappear just because the team was forbidden to play. The taste of the goal would remain. The pleasure of telling how your champions had crushed the others and the wish to remember great moves in the game would not disappear. Passing by word of mouth, the illicit enjoyment would be increased. An ordinary football match would become popular history. It would become a kind of epic, like the stories handed down which take on mythical status.

'We will have to take another route,' said Eberhardt turning to the other officials, 'something which in a definitive way will take from these dogs the idea that they are the best. They must return to being absolutely nothing!'

This last word resonated in the room like a rifle shot, like a sharp blow that concedes no conditions. The Nazi let the word resonate a little longer as he held his back upright, before breathing his diabolical solution.

'A defeat is required,' he said, 'so therefore we need to play. But we must play astutely against this team, who have shown themselves to be so good. We will need our best football team in circulation to beat them, to humiliate them, to show them in such a way that they cannot hope for any kind of redemption.'

The officials gave a sharp intake of breath. One word seemed obvious to all: Flakelf.

'We will call Flakelf, the unbeatable team of the Wehrmacht,' said Eberhardt finally articulating the common whispers. 'We'll play the match in the Dynamo stadium and we'll beat them. We will publicise the match extensively, forcing the Ukrainians to recognise our superior strength with their own eyes.'

In the following days newspapers and radio announced the arrival of the unbeatable German team. On the walls around Kiev appeared flyers advertising the great encounter between Flakelf, the German armed forces team, and Start, made up of local players.

Josif Kordik gathered his men to the bread factory. Their faces were tense and dark and a troubled mood circled in the air.

'My friends,' started the manager, 'you can't hide the fact that this undertaking smells of death. From whatever angle I look at it I can't see anything good. This is the position: to be beaten and forever be slaves or to win and keep fighting to the end. As I know the Nazis, they will not accept defeat without reprisals. It is a test of strength and they want to show who is strongest. To win would mean death.'

In the narrow space of the courtyard, in the dark of night, Kordik's words had a ghostly ring to them. It was a deadly game, a huge trap in which they had been ensnared by their own skill.

'You must all excuse me,' continued Kordik with a cracked voice. 'I ask you to forgive me for having the idea to put the team together, for asking you to make such a choice. I was thinking of redemption, of how I know you can play with the ball. Instead I've put you in a madman's game. I'm sending you to the butcher.'

The group of men remained seated, silently listening to his words. Only Trusevich spoke up. In the icy moonlight the goalkeeper spoke of a tomorrow which already seemed to be lost:

'I don't feel beaten. It's not right to think that we are in the wrong.

It's the oppressors who are constricting us to die. I have no choice Josif, there is nothing else to do. I'm a goalkeeper and I can only make saves. Would any one of you ever take the field with the intention of deliberately misplacing a pass?'

There was no discussion. No one needed courage to understand what they had to do.

That night the goalkeeper dreamt of playing a strange match on a pitch on an incline. When the ball was kicked by his teammates it fell behind him and he hurt himself in trying to catch hold of it. By the end of the game he was able to save every shot that came towards him. He was worn out and wearing a shirt soaked in a sweat that was curiously similar to blood. Opposite the goal he now saw Death; elegant, kind and darkly dressed.

'I must kick for the last time,' said Death calmly arranging the position of the ball. 'I love to act and talk with a certain... rigour.'

With a smile he kicked the ball from the penalty spot. As Nikolai dived to attempt a save he was hit by a torrent of blows, a hail of machine gun fire. He woke up suddenly, the air almost hot, his forehead sweating. Between his hands he was twisting the pillow filled with straw.

The scheduled date was 6 August. The stadium seemed like a crowded town square, an unending arena divided into two colours. In the best seats on one side, the green of the Nazi uniforms stood out. The rest of the stadium was a mass of Ukrainians with their hope, hunger and a dark misery which, in that moment, was suspended for a festival.

Trusevich led Start out to cautious applause and went straight to the centre circle. Loud cheers greeted the great Flakelf as they took to the field. The match started and the script was followed exactly as the Germans ran hard throwing themselves forward, surrounding Start, putting them under siege.

From his area in front of the line which marked out life and death, Nikolai Trusevich contributed to the cause. He watched opponents arrive on the run. With his eyes he followed the flight of the ball as it was crossed from one side of the pitch to the other. 'This time it's a massacre,' he thought as he sent the ball back into play. 'We won't be able to withstand this continuous assault.'

The Ukrainians were weak, prisoners to hunger, forced labour and extreme pressure, while the other team raced about the pitch like voracious wolves. Little time had passed, about ten minutes, when a header from the Nazi centre forward whizzed towards the crossbar like a thunderbolt. Nikolai launched himself, almost into flight. Slowly, as though made of stone his arm raised itself in the direction of the ball. His hand seemed to weigh more than a ton. From the shouts of the Germans he realised that the ball must have crossed the line.

Goncharenko passed by his side and leant down to collect the ball. There was no need for any words; just a look, a bitter grimace. A deep wound. Then, with the ball in his hand, Makar Goncharenko started towards the centre of the pitch to restart the game. He walked slowly and with composure. Sitting at the base of his goalpost, Trusevich watched that peaceful walk as though he was catching a glimpse of a dream. The other players, the referee, the whole stadium had stopped to watch that player who walked slowly across the ground. He held the ball in his hands with the serene look on his face of someone who did not feel himself to be defeated. It was then that from the Ukrainian part of the stadium the first muffled applause could be heard, closely followed by more and more until it became a wave of sound.

When play restarted, Trusevich knew that he could not give up. The equalising goal arrived soon afterwards. Before the end of the first half, Goncharenko escaped towards the by line and crossed the ball to the centre. It passed the defenders and rolled towards Balakhin who was running at full tilt. The Ukrainian player looked up towards the goal and caught the worried stare of the German keeper. He saw the great space of the goalmouth appear before him and, in the silence into which he seemed to have plunged the stadium, he recognised death. Deep within he did not have time to make a calculation. With an open goal a player has no time to speculate, he can only shoot. Balakhin shot, blasting the ball into the middle of the net to give them the lead.

It was not a case of heroism or even of courage he thought as he embraced his team mates. You wanted to play, he thought, and you have played.

In the stands the Ukrainians had refound their breath, despite the protests and insults of the Germans. Someone in the main stand moved suddenly, took hold of a rifle and started to make threats. On the pitch, the referee motioned to say that for now that was enough.

During the half-time break Commandant Fischer of the Gestapo went into the Ukrainians' changing room to speak to them.

'That was really very good, congratulations,' he said with a glassy smile. 'You want to show the people watching that you can play, and you have certainly demonstrated this. Perhaps you are thick in the head, perhaps you don't understand. Now we have the second half, forty-five minutes to recover. Make sure you go carefully. This is not advice, it is an order,' he said, holding a Luger in his hand.

With the score at 3–2 the local public had difficulty in holding back their joy as the Nazis lost themselves in a cloud of black rage. The situation had become a paradox: from one side of the stadium came the muted euphoria, a longed-for feeling of contentment; from the other side a grotesque bawling, furious shouts and threatening gunshots. On the pitch Start seemed to be dancing, playing fast and with skilful artistry. After about half an hour came the fourth goal, and the referee, thinking of the embarrassment, perhaps afraid that he had not played his own part sufficiently, perhaps thinking of his own fate, decided that the match had run its course.

Start left the pitch slowly. To a little brave applause they made their way to the changing room. Nobody uttered a word. In a surreal atmosphere, with heads lowered, the eleven men passed through the crowd who either hailed them with a look or spat at and insulted them. On the wooden benches, among the sweaty shirts, Sukharev sang a little song. Josif Kordik lit a cigarette and thought that now everything was accomplished. When Major General Eberhardt sent for him he felt he must be condemned.

The face of the Nazi had turned black. With deep contempt he turned to the other man:

'Today has gone well for you. You've been lucky. Flakelf were tired. I also think you really do not understand that I really am not joking.

This will be written off as a freak event so it doesn't count. The match will be replayed and since you need to learn, you are all under arrest. You will play again on the 15th.'

Tears rolled down Kordik's face as he stood opposite the Nazi. To the contemptuous words from the official the baker raised an objection:

'It's not a question of fear General, it's for my players and the price they will have to pay. You can replay the match a thousand times and victory will continue to go to them. This will happen if you keep on playing. There is no other solution other than to shoot.'

Kordik had said the word, and the word had been held by the official. Any mention of the first defeat was forbidden. No newspapers or radio could mention that eleven filthy prisoners had made their oppressors look foolish. They were a team of eleven champions who went on to win the second match. This time the Gestapo arrived in the changing room as the match had just finished. They dished out blows and kicked the players as if they were balls. Some were arrested and sent to the camp at Baby Yar .

Nikolai Trusevich was dragged into the middle of the street still wearing the shirt, and was killed with a shot to the neck from an official. The executioner was a Bavarian grocer, big and jolly. At home he had an aged mother and older brother who kept the shop going. He was a practical soul; work and save. He had always worked hard to make the most of things. Faced with this goalkeeper, still in his football kit he thought just one shot would suffice. To kill a man, a shot is more than enough. It is enough to shoot straight at the head without a thought. So he went to Trusevich's side and said to the champion:

'Now see if you can save this.'

He was a practical soul who lacked imagination. So he would never know that as the bullet left the pistol, Trusevich saw it coming fast and straight on his right, and he dived to make a save.

A Pa'

I believe that you must give of yourself to the end,
and that you must also make mistakes.

PIER PAOLO PASOLINI

On the afternoon of July 4 1954 Pier Paolo Pasolini left his house at exactly three o'clock in the afternoon. The sun burned down on Rome and melted the few pedestrians, turning them into daylight phantoms. The air was so immobile and silent, that Pasolini thought nothing could possibly be happening at this time. The world seemed to have been stopped, as after a nuclear explosion, boiled by the heat of a huge bomb which had liquefied all living things as easily as if they had been made of ice.

Keeping close to walls to take advantage of any shade, Pasolini went up via Ostiense near the city centre, where the sheets covering the skeletons of the buildings under construction reminded him of sails hoisted to catch a non-existent breeze. Walking nearer to them, he found the street had been dug up and dust and stones lay about. A thin pink coating of something like talcum powder covered everything. Next to the first and biggest building, a heap of rubble hid a hole made by an excavation, which would be filled by the foundations for a new building, but was currently like a large tooth in the ground with a huge cavity. It was Sunday and the yard was deserted. Everything seemed suspended and still.

'A truce,' thought Pasolini, 'there is no war here today.'

But as he was watching this spot, absorbing the silence where the city was being reborn, all of a sudden he heard a shout muffled through gritted teeth as though someone did not really want that silence to be broken.

'Get a move on Spi, or we're gonna be here all night,' said a voice that seemed to be coming from an oldish man. 'Start passing me the stuff, and be quick about it.'

Gingerly Pasolini climbed up the rubble, being careful not to make any noise. He lay down at the top of the mound, so as to secretly observe what was happening.

'I'll be like those Red Indians,' he thought as he stretched out on the mound. 'I'll watch and listen, but they won't spot me.'

On the edge of the large hole the yard's fencing began; an expanse of iron sheets fixed to wooden poles, to keep the construction area separate. Further down from where he was looking, Pasolini noticed a gap in the metal sheeting, like a fold on the corner of a piece of paper. Next to this gap, with his back facing Pasolini, stood a man in a vest who was built like a tank. It was certainly this chap who had spoken, and when he turned he looked nervous and agitated. He looked around impatiently, his hand repeatedly touching his leg, and with the other hand he smoothed the stubble on his cheeks, as if to reassure himself not to worry.

After a few minutes, from behind the metal sheets, Pasolini heard a noise of something being dragged along, then a light whistle as though a sparrow had started to sing. At that sound, the man darted down towards the opening in the fence, then he grabbed hold of something and started to pull. In an instant, like a conjurer, there appeared in his hands a large iron bar that he placed very carefully on the barrow resting nearby.

'I've got it Spi,' he called back into the hole in a half whisper. 'Chuck me through whatever you find and then we'll be off.'

From the other side of the fence someone was continuing to pass wooden beams and other construction materials through the opening, so that in a couple of minutes the barrow was fully loaded. After some minutes Pasolini heard the man in the vest say, 'Come on,' as he started to push the barrow towards the street.

He went past, below Pasolini, perspiring on the mound, from where he could see beads of sweat on the man's forehead, his muscles straining with effort as he pushed the cart. He kept watching until the cart disappeared around a corner, to be absorbed back into the world without a second thought.

When he turned back to the gap in the fence, he could see a lad of about twelve years old next to the large hole. He was slim and sweating, with his head resting on his chest as if he had just nodded off to sleep.

Pasolini watched the boy for a few moments, thinking that it was not such a good idea to be hanging around where a robbery had just taken place. Apart from that, he was rather worried by the stillness of the boy with his back to the fence, with his head lolling as though he had been shot. Pasolini wondered if the boy needed help, so he went down from his hillock, wiping the dust from his trousers, and then turned away from the rubble towards the boy. He walked cautiously, convinced that if the boy saw him coming he would run away in fright. A guilty conscience after a crime would usually lead to a hasty escape, reasoned Pasolini. As he grew near to the boy, he could see no signs that he was getting ready to run. Hearing the crunch of Pasolini's footsteps on the gravel, the boy lifted his head a little, and gave a sidelong glance towards the noise, before returning his head to its resting position on his chest.

Standing opposite the boy, Pasolini was unsure what to do. He sat down next to him, with his back to the fence, and took in the situation. From deep in the lad's chest he heard a scraping sound, the rough sound of someone gasping for air. His stripy shirt was drenched in sweat and stuck to his ribs as he struggled to breathe. This touched Pasolini to the core, and he was afraid that this skinny, frail lad would pass away right there, in front of him.

'Are you all right?' he asked anxiously.

The boy nodded a couple of times before saying:

'I've got asthma, and sometimes I have trouble breathing. This dust, and this heat is terrible for me. Every so often the asthma come and grabs me, and then in a while it goes away.'

'Perhaps you've been overdoing it, those were heavy things you were lifting and in this heat you get short of breath even when you're sitting still,' said Pasolini kindly, in a tone of voice that let the boy know that he had seen what had happened, but that he need not be worried.

The boy did not react. He remained still and the rasping breaths were now beginning to ease. They stayed like this for some moments, the only noise coming from the boy's wheezing, until he broke the silence saying:

'What are you looking for round here? Why are you spying on people as they are doing their work?'

This was said with a half smile on his face, as if saying that he was prepared to consider trusting Pasolini, but he was going to tread carefully.

'I'm not looking for anything, I'm just going for a walk,' said Pasolini returning a smile. 'I like to float about between the buildings under construction, like this one here, to think what they used to be like, and to imagine how they will be when the work is completed. I walk about immersed in my own thoughts, and often I come across pleasant surprises. Houses raised up from nothing; strange streets, people who come to live in a place and make new acquaintances. Now and again I find quite unexpected things. Like today for example, I found you... working.'

'Yeah, so what? I've gotta live. I'll fill up the barrow for Pazzo[1] and keep my mouth shut. I need a few lire to eat,' said the boy decisively, looking Pasolini straight in the eye as if explaining something quite natural that only he, in his ignorance, did not know about and would certainly not know how to carry out.

Pasolini was struck by the boy's gaze, by the determination and strength of this carefree imp. In that moment he felt himself to be really alive. Amidst the dust and the ghosts of the building shells, he had just been taught something he did not realise he still had to learn. Something ugly can also contain beauty; something foul smelling may also possess an unusual perfume; someone can be fully alive though he fights hard for every breath. Pasolini said nothing more, as his smile widened, his head leaning against the metal sheet, its warmth burning his cheek, and soothing his neck and shoulders.

'My name is Renatino, but everyone calls me Spino, because I'm so thin and tough[2], if you understand me,' said the boy holding out

1 Pazzo translates as 'madman' or, colloquially, 'nutter'.
2 *Spino* is the Italian word for a thorn tree.

110

his arm.

'I'm Pier Paolo, and that is what I'm known as,' replied Pasolini, exchanging a strong, sweaty handshake.

This was the start of a great friendship between Pasolini and Renato Panizza, known as Spino, one blazing day in July, with only the buildings under construction as witnesses to the understanding between a poet and a young boy.

They talked for a long time that afternoon about Spino's family, originally from the sparse countryside of Abruzzo, who had come to Rome to try and make a better life. Spino talked of his small home in Monteverde, of his shortness of breath, which would never leave him in peace. He also talked of football, which was his real passion. They found many things in common, despite at first glance being from such different backgrounds. The poet also loved to play football, and at great length they debated teams, formations and the best way to start a counter-attack.

A couple of hours later, with the sun now lower in the sky, Spino asked Pasolini, if he had nothing else to do, whether he would like to accompany him to Monteverde to a patch of waste ground behind the flats under construction, where he was going to meet his gang: Catena, Manetta, Montesano and the others who were coming for a match.

'I'd love to Spino, but only if I can get a game myself. I'm quite handy, and at left wing I'm brilliant, if I say so myself. Can you do the Biavati double step?' said Pasolini, standing up to trap an imaginary ball with a gentle caress of the foot.

Then he ran ahead, quick and nimble, and whacked a small stone with a powerful shot which hit the metal sheeting and rebounded off it with a sound like a Chinese gong.

'Bloody hell Pa', I can see you're quite tasty, but you're better off showing the lads these skills with a proper ball when we get to the match. Hurry up, we're late. Move your arse.'

When they reached the waste ground at Monteverde, a dozen or so lads were already chasing around after a ball. Spino called over to Manetta, a tall hefty lad who seemed to be in charge, and presented Pasolini to him:

'Mane' this is a mate of mine, he's a pretty good player. He's a left wing, but he says he can play in midfield.'

Manetta looked Pasolini up and down, then shook his hand saying, 'It's all right with me, the pitch is big, so one more nutter won't make any difference.'

Then he called to Catena and said, 'Go and pick the teams and make a start before it gets dark. I'm knackered already.'

So the lads gathered in the centre of the pitch and the teams were picked. Spino put himself in goal because of his asthma; Pasolini went out on the wing, on the same side of the pitch as Manetta. The match started, and it was more of a fight than a game of football. The players frantically followed the ball in a *mattanza* of kicking legs[3]. Soon the space between the buildings was filled with echoing shouts, calls for the ball, reproaches and colourful oaths. In the middle of all the mayhem, only Pasolini tried to give some sense to the play. He stuck patiently to his wing, calling for the ball, and when it finally came to him he didn't just want to run with it towards the goal. Instead, he looked up, gestured about the field, shouted instructions to teammates to find space before he distributed the ball with efficiency.

Perhaps it was because he was an adult; perhaps it was because of the passion which he put into the match, even though it was not an important final, that the lads saw Pasolini as a kind of cool madman, a species of prophet from afar who had come to explain the mysteries of football to them. Amidst the chaos, playing behind his guide, Manetta for the first time really understood how to play. He learnt that it was not always worth charging after the ball like a mad bullock every time it was in front of you. Using Pasolini as a wall, he could make a triangle and exchange passes, before a herd of other lads descended on him. He would receive the ball again and, after looking where Montesano or Brutto had moved, he could decide on how to weight his pass.

As they sat on the grass after the match, completely exhausted, Manetta asked the poet if he would like come back every so often

3 *mattanza*: the slaughter of tuna fish

for a game.

'I'd like to make a real team,' Manetta said, 'with Spino in goal and nine other fellas on the pitch. A proper team, do you know what I mean? You could play on the left wing, and be our coach. We'd all get involved: me, Catena, Montesano, Brutto, Zoppo, Remo, More', Spino and Agnolo Pugnetta[4]. We'd scare the other teams around Monteverde, and even give teams from further off a run for their money.'

Pasolini accepted willingly. He said it would be a pleasure. They shook hands and, with many slaps on the back, went their separate ways, but not before an appointment had been arranged. In three days the lads would gather again to sort out further details. In the meantime they would try to find another group of lads who they could challenge to a match.

As Pasolini left in the direction of Ostiense, Spino shouted to him from some metres away:

'Hey Pa', we don't have a name. You've got a way with words, give us a hand. What shall we call our team?'

Someone from the gang said it should be called 'Sons of Whores' which made everyone laugh. Other suggestions were discarded, until the group fell silent and they looked towards the poet who seemed to be turning something over in his mind.

'I suggest we call the team 'Chaos'; that seems appropriate to me, not only for our style of play, but also for the situation we find ourselves in,' said Pasolini looking around at the flats, the mounds of concrete and the rubbish that lay around the barren field. 'Chaos also means confusion, the confusion which all of us come from, from which the earth was made, so they say, from where everything was born and where everything ends up.'

This was how, with the sun setting behind the blocks of flats, that a poet and ten lads founded the Chaos football team from Monteverde.

---

4 Some of the boys' names are nicknames which translate roughly thus: Manetta: full throttle; Catena: chain; Brutto: ugly; Zoppo: lame; Remo: oar; More': dark-skinned; Pugnetta: punchy, tough.

Pasolini kept his word. At least two evenings a week, he would go to the waste ground where Spino and Manetta's gang were waiting. Often he tried to teach them a few tactics – with some difficulty, because the youths were true to their name and unused to listening and using self-control. It would take time, patience, repeated requests, arguments, shouts and quarrels to make a decent outfit of them. Nonetheless, the lads with such troubled lives played the game with intense passion. After the games, they would gather around the fountain in silence for a few minutes, or Pasolini would talk about the feats of the great Bologna team he had seen as a boy, who he had loved as though they played within the intangible beauty of a dream.

'You know,' he said to the weary lads, 'playing football is like painting, or composing poetry or writing a story. For this reason it is played with such passion. Each of you has his own way of running, of passing the ball, of making a tackle, and when someone is able to actually carry out the intentions in his mind, then he feels fulfilled. This is the beauty of the game.'

In a few weeks Chaos were quite a promising team, with some cohesion and a clear formation. They were simply ten lads and a poet with a passion for football, who up until that time had not played against real opponents. One evening Catena spoke to Pasolini:

'Now Pa' it seems that we're a pretty strong outfit, but we're always playing against the kids round Monteverde, and they're not up to much. Let's see if we can organise a proper game with a team from somewhere else, an away match,' he said as he took a gulp from the fountain.

Among themselves the lads thought this was the right moment to test themselves. At the end of August, Pasolini started discussions with a team who played in Ostiense. This team was made up of kids of about fifteen years old, who did not like the idea of taking on a team who had a man as one of the players. Pasolini brought Manetta with him for further negotiations about the match. The conversation became rather heated, and a decision about the match started to drift into the distance, until the Ostiense boys came up with the idea of using the brother of Filipetto Giordano, who did jobs for shopkeepers lifting heavy goods, was built like a tank and was thirty years old.

'You're raving mad,' said Filipetto with a wave of derision towards Manetta.

'Maybe so,' replied Manetta, negotiating hard, 'but you don't know what Chaos of Monteverde are about. We are a pure force. We use the famous Bologna system. We've got a left wing who's like a jet plane and two top-class half-backs. We don't just play football sunshine, we are poetry in motion.'

The match took place on 30 August 1954, and was the start of a long series of victories for the Chaos team. Their debut away match did not go completely smoothly, for despite the advice from their captain, Manetta, the others let their nerves get the better of them. Brutto, in midfield, lost the ball a couple of times under pressure from opponents, to howls and oaths from his teammates. They let in a soft goal when a distracted Spino did not notice a back pass from Zoppo which put the Ostiense striker Duccio Papale in front of goal, from where his powerful shot went in off the post, sending the home crowd wild.

Pasolini did not lose heart. He knew the strength of his players, and when he saw their morale drop after the goal he asked Brutto to play on the wing so that he could direct the midfield and make other players get involved in the game. So, with his example, the team started to believe in themselves again, and regain some of their flair. Catena scored, so did Montesano; Manetta scored twice and Pasolini himself once. This last goal was a shot caught on the volley off a long pass from Brutto. The match ended 5-2, a great triumph, not just for the result, but because of the comeback after conceding a goal, and also for the team's character and style of play. Even those who were watching, who had been hostile and whistled at first, recognised the quality of the team, of those lads who now felt like champions.

Some weeks later, a rather embarrassed Filipetto Giordano went back to Manetta to ask for a rematch, which Chaos won 8-1. After that they beat Testaccio easily 6-0, and then a thumping 5-1 against Garbatella on the pitch behind St Peter's basilica. The return match was a massacre at 8-3.

The fame of this team spread throughout the districts of Rome, and reached as far as Ostia on the coast. One afternoon, Pasolini was chatting with the restaurant owner Luigi Orlandi, known as Giggio, at Bagno Ondina. Nearby a group of foreign tourists were getting organised for a game of beach football. They were English lads who wanted to take on the locals who were not really in the mood to play. The English were strong, skilful and fit, able to run rings round the Romans. Soon the sunbathers on the beach began to watch, shouting encouragement and insults, laughing and getting involved in the action. Pasolini too became absorbed, enjoying the game in the midst of the mayhem it had created. It was when Giggio Orlandi lamented to Pasolini about the feeble way in which the Italians were playing, of their lack of passion and their poor skills, that the poet told him about the Chaos team from Monteverde.

Orlandi listened to his friend, and then came out with a suggestion.

'Why don't you bring them down here to play at the Idroscalo? There's a lethal team down here, and I'd like to see what your boys can do against our Ostia lads. They're about eighteen years old, and really sharp. I'll provide a trophy for the winners. We'll call it the 'Lido Trophy'; it'll be quite something, you'll see.'

The match was fixed for 10 September, to be played on the Idroscalo pitch. When Pasolini told the rest of the team they were a bit worried.

'But Pa', they'll be really good, they're bigger than us and they're bound to be rough!'

'Have you forgotten what sort of a team we are? That we keep fighting to the last. We've shown several times before that we are very well organised. In life you have to take risks, you have to use all the reserves of strength that you have within you, you have to be prepared to run the risk of making mistakes,' put in Pasolini, and at this the lads were convinced.

On the Idroscalo pitch at Ostia Chaos from Monteverde played the match which really sealed their reputation. Giggio Orlandi had managed to locate some proper football jerseys, although some of the sizes did not fit exactly. Remo and Pugnetta played with their sleeves rolled up, and a thick string tied round the socks, much to the mirth of the spectators. Manetta, tall and lean, was given a jersey that finished just above his navel, so perhaps because of this, or perhaps because the challenge ahead seemed too daunting, he sidled up to Pasolini before they took to the pitch and said;

'Hey Pa', you can be skipper; I don't feel like it today.'

Pasolini went to the centre circle to meet the referee Moricone, and to shake hands with the other captain. Against the light from a baking sun, the poet saw the shadow of a slim lad moving towards him with a light, graceful gait. He had thick curly hair, two big blue eyes, and the refined good looks seen in paintings that can take your breath away.

'Pleased to meet you, I'm Ricetto,' he said offering a hand. 'We're ready to start, and for you the match is already over,' he added with an unnervingly confident grin.

Having won the toss, Pasolini said something in reply, then chose the half of the pitch Chaos were to defend in the first half. Feeling rather shaky, he returned the handshakes of the referee and the opposing captain.

Pasolini played well throughout the match, pushing himself to the limit as usual. But each time he went near to the opponents' penalty area he could not bring himself to look at Ricetto, who was their goalkeeper. Ricetto watched the play with his deep blue eyes which took Pasolini's breath away. He made himself call for the ball and speak to his teammates, to keep his mind on the game.

The Idroscalo from Ostia were really sharp, but so were the Chaos in reply. Although Ostia were more skilful and better organised, the lads from Monteverde played with all their heart, running and battling to the end.

The match was on a knife-edge. Ostia had scored first, to be followed by a goal from Catena, which was worthy of the great Parola. Then Martini scored for Ostia, before Moretto equalised from a free kick. Pasolini himself scored with a long-range shot, before the home team made the score even from a penalty given for Pugnetta's handball.

At the end of normal time, after all the drama of the match, the score was still even. The referee called both captains to the centre circle and said, 'For extra time we'll play two halves of a quarter of an hour, after which one of you will have won the cup.' But even after this, with each side scoring once again, the match was still undecided. So Moricone, the referee, called Giggio Orlandi over and said:

'What are we supposed to do? If someone is to win the cup today, we'll have to have penalties. This would happen in an international. Each side takes five, and the team who scores most is the winner.'

Giggio nodded his assent, and the match continued.

The home side took the first shot and scored. Remo put his penalty wide of the goal. The desperation felt by the Chaos team was quite visible, while the Ostia fans roared with relief. After the next round of penalties the score was once again even, as a home player missed, and Chaos kept the scores even up to the final round where Spino saved a lethal shot from Andreucci, who had aimed to the right-hand corner of the goal. Chaos needed to seize this moment. Spino's teammates started to celebrate, with back-slapping, hugs and kisses that ran the risk of becoming overwhelming. With the scores level, it was Pasolini with the duty of taking the final and decisive kick.

The poet took the ball in both hands, squeezing it so hard it almost burst, then he bounced it a few times as he tried to concentrate and collect his thoughts. What does a footballer think at such a moment? Is the mind completely clear, or is it so full of terror that everything is thrown away in an instant? The distance is only eleven metres, with the goal ahead seeming immense, but even managing an ordinary pass with the ball can be an ordeal. On that night at the Idroscalo pitch, Pasolini was Chaos, he was the hopes of ten lads who had their dream tied to his feet, to that one penalty kick. He had ten lads inside himself, inside his being, while in front of him gazed those mesmerising deep blue eyes.

The poet placed the ball carefully on the penalty spot, and took two paces back to make the ground even for his run up. Then he ran up and shot without looking where he was aiming. The ball whizzed into the net and he heard a roar as Manetta, Spino, Catena and the others jumped up in ecstasy. As his team were going mad in a whirl of embraces, jumping on each other in a heap, he noticed Ricetto still lying flat on his back on the goal line.

Giggio Orlandi came up with the trophy as he had promised. The Chaos team from Monteverde now felt like real football stars. Pasolini walked over towards the Ostia keeper with his heart thumping.

'I'm really sorry,' he said.

The lad was crying. Pasolini's ears heard the shouts of joy, and he saw the tears in the eyes of the beaten goalkeeper.

From somewhere deep inside, Pasolini felt a sense that in fact he had lost everything.

The Duty of Taking a Penalty

The face of Bitossi as he loses the World Cycling Championship by half a metre. His steady movement towards an approaching finish line on the gentle incline of the home straight at Gap. A finish line which will always be far away and will take a piece of his life, while Basso his teammate will steal the world title.

The tears of Ale on the day Meroni[1] died, squashed under a car like a cat. He cried in silence, sobbing with the pain of real anguish. The television that evening in black and white, with Meroni's crop of hair like The Beatles. His socks forever rolled halfway down.

Matches on the radio. Niccolo' Carosio[2]. The pitch in various shades on the first small screens. The surprise of the brightness of light in the stadium, everything in colour, a triumph of splendour and noise.

Giando talking of the great Torino. He spoke of them with love, first reciting the formation in a litany of names, magical words before the players took the field for the challenge. Like me he was a boy who had never seen them play, neither Mazzola or Loik or Bacigalupo. Yet biting into a snack he would assure you he had seen them play hundreds of times. Valentino with his raking pass across the pitch; the strength of Gabetto; Maroso with his chest upright

1 Gigi Meroni: Italian footballer with Genoa and Torino. A great individualist who was tragically run over and killed in October 1967 aged 24.

2 Niccolo' Carosio was an Italian radio sports commentator.

3 Alessandro Mazzinghi and Kim Soo Kim. They boxed for the super welterweight world title in front of 60,000 people at the San Siro stadium in Milan on 26 May 1968. After an exhausting fight lasting 15 rounds, Mazzinghi was eventually champion.

among the crowd. It does not matter at all to me if it was all made up, if Giando invented all the matches. The names of those mythical players were already part of history. I would listen to their imaginary actions, listening enthralled with my heart in my mouth. That was our epic. It was our action replay.

Mazzinghi and the Korean in the slaughter house of San Siro[3]. His tired face, his gaze lost in the snare of boxing for rounds that don't just last three minutes but months, whole years.

Gilles[4] somersaulting as he took off towards the sky and landed against a net like a football in a goal. A squashed paper bag on a street corner.

Simpson[5] climbing, falling, getting up, falling again, as you probably fall in an unending dream on Mont Ventoux where you know you must stay and pedal. For Simpson I took a bad mark in school, for a reply which I gave on Monte Ventoso which was actually by Petrarch, but for me was the grave of a man who broke down in the middle of a climb. The teacher did not understand and she really laid into me almost starting to shout:

'We are talking about literature, not cycling,' she said, 'this is no joking matter.'

Still today I keep these faces before me. In my mind I arrange the strongest team formations before I fall asleep at night. I organise my team of world-class players, dreaming of great moves until sleep arrives, though fear does not leave me. Every now and again I put myself in the team between Garrincha and Cruyff, between Platini and Maradona.

Sick and displaced I continued to do this at the end of my first life. It was 1990 and I was in hospital. Baggio[6] however was playing for the national team. In my thoughts I made him score an amazing goal against all the odds. Then they reattached my heart. It's not a

4 Gilles Villeneuve: Canadian Formula 1 driver who died on 8 May 1982, qualifying for the Belgian Grand Prix.
5 Tom Simpson: English cyclist who died in the blazing heat of Mont Ventoux on 13 July during the 1967 Tour de France.
6 Roberto Baggio: Italian footballer from 1980s to early 2000s. He played with Vicenza, Fiorentina, Juventus, Milan, Bologna, Inter and Brescia.

question of courage, you don't have much choice with that kind of thing. You live or you die. A bit like a big final. A bit like the duty of taking a penalty.

So it is that I have decided to write these stories which emerge from hazy memories and dreams. Stories which are both real and imaginary, like those told me by Giando as he bit into a sandwich.

Dramatis Personae

FAUSTO COPPI

He was born in a village between Tortona and Nove Ligure at five o'clock in the afternoon on 15 September 1919. Until he was fourteen years old he was a farm labourer like his parents, at which point he took the job as errand boy for a butcher's shop in Novi. It was here that he started riding a bicycle. In 1938 he competed in his first races as an amateur. He turned professional in 1940 and quickly won the Giro d'Italia. Making his mark on all the major races across Europe, he came to be known as 'il Campionissimo' (the great champion). He was a complete racing cyclist; a strong climber also capable of great time trials as when, in 1942, he took the hour record from Maurice Archimbaud. He was a very thin man with two large sunken eyes either side of a sharp nose, and the incredible lung capacity of seven litres. Coppi ushered in the modern era of cycling, introducing specialised preparation and diets. He made his mark on sporting history with achievements at the highest level. His use of certain medical practices

led to fierce controversy with his great rival Gino Bartali. Coppi died tragically at 8.45 on 1 January 1960. During a race in Africa he contracted a form of malaria which Italian doctors failed to recognise. This bizarre death has contributed to the legend, to the myth of a champion. The radio broadcaster Mario Ferretti immortalised Coppi with the phrase: 'One man is in the lead, his shirt is pale blue and white, his name is Fausto Coppi.'

Fausto Coppi wins the
Tour de France, July 1949

127

GUY MOLL

Moll soared like a meteor in the world of motor racing. He only competed for one season, 1934, but he left indelible memories on those who saw him race. Enzo Ferrari in his memoirs, Le Briglie del Successo (The Reins of Success), viewed Moll as one of the greatest drivers of all time. With a Spanish mother, and a French father who emigrated to Algeria, Moll was one of the few drivers able to be compared with Tazio Nuvolari, for his aggression and his carefree style in the face of the most extreme danger. He made his debut at Monte Carlo, where he won this most difficult Grand Prix on the final lap, and died at the Pescara circuit while taking part in the Coppa Acerbo, in circumstances which remain murky. It was 15 August, and Moll was just twenty-four years old.

Guy Moll, 1934

THE GREAT TORINO FOOTBALL TEAM

Bacigalupo, Ballarin, Rigamonti, Maroso, Grezar, Castigliano, Ossola, Loik, Gabetto, Mazzola, Ferraris, Menti. They were an exceptional team. Even today their achievements are amazing. Between 1942 and 1949 they were practically invincible, winning five championships consecutively. At home they were unbeaten from 17 January 1940; out of 93 matches 83 were won and 10 drawn. Without the interruption of the Second World War they would probably have reached even greater heights.

Torino played at the small stadium in via Filadelfia, a maroon-coloured cauldron where opponents met an inevitable fate. As railwayman Bormida blew his trumpet, the captain Valentino Mazzola would roll up his sleeves. This was the signal to attack. They could overcome any unfavourable situation in a match. The strength of the team was demonstrated by the fact that ten of the eleven players were Italian internationals. On the afternoon of 4 May 1949, returning from a match in Portugal, the plane returning to Turin crashed against the boundary wall of the Superga Basilica, on a hill overlooking the city. There were no survivors. From that day the myth of a team of invincible champions was born.

Torino team group: (back row, left to right) Eusebio Castigliano, Aldo Ballarin, Mario Rigamonti, Enzo Loik, Virgilio Maroso, Valentino Mazzola; (front row, left to right) Valerio Bacigalupo, Romeo Menti, Franco Ossola, Danilo Martelli, Guglielmo Gabetto, 31 October 1948

129

GARRINCHA

His full name was Manuel Francisco dos Santos. He was born on 26 October 1933 in Pau Grande, a shanty town about thirty kilometres outside Rio. As a small child he was struck by polio, which left his legs thin and unsteady. Despite the efforts of a doctor, and his own fierce determination, he did not regain complete use of his legs which remained misshapen. As a result, his family nicknamed him Garrincha, the passerotto (little sparrow) with the twisted legs. He was sixteen years old when the great full back Nilton Santos first saw him play, and immediately recognised how his unique dummy was so deadly. He had a trial with Botafogo, the team where he was to start his amazing career that included two world cup victories, and ensured him legendary status in the history of football. His dribbling – always the same but always irresistible – sent the crowds delirious, and his style became known as 'l'allegria della gente'. He was a simple man, almost naive in his outlook, seeing people without cynicism, letting himself be guided by his natural openness. His decline was sad and miserable, marked by his stormy love affair with the singer Elsa Soares. Becoming overweight and unwell, his last years were spent between melancholy exhibitions of his old flair, and the abysses of alcohol abuse. Alone and largely forgotten, death caught up with him on 20 January 1983.

Garrincha in Brazil strip, November 1961

JACK JOHNSON

Jack Johnson was born on 31 March 1878 in Galveston Texas. As a boy he worked in he cotton fields and then as a stevedore in the city's port. He moved about the state of Texas working as a stable hand and a trainer in various gyms. He first discovered boxing while watching Joe Walcott training in Boston. In 1899 he began a career which would last almost 30 years and take him to the top of the world's boxing ranks after beating Tommy Burns in a classic encounter. Many critics have viewed him as the greatest heavyweight in boxing history. He was very large, strong, well co-ordinated, a great stylist, a man with a great punching rhythm and a master of the art of the feint. He fought 114 times losing on just seven occasions. Jack Johnson was a controversial figure. Always extrovert, he often toured the USA at the wheel of a sporty Dusemberg with a glamorous blonde at his side, a

fact which created a furore in a country that was often fiercely racist. Johnson loved to dress with great care and attention to detail. He played the double bass with a smile which his enemies considered the contempt-uous leer of a braggart. He died on 10 June 1946 after a road accident. A few weeks before he died he had been in the ring once more for an exhibition against his great rival Joe Jeanette. He was sixty-eight years old.

Jack Johnson

131

TAZIO NUVOLARI

He was born at Casteldario in the province of Mantua on 16 November 1892. He was short, slender and gifted with amazing courage which allowed him to blend technical ability with a capacity to take risks. A sublime driver in any vehicle and over any type of course, he gave his utmost in any circumstances. His innumerable races have taken on legendary status, symbolic of a particular era in motor sport. Tazio started to drive a Turcaimer motorbike at thirteen years old, then a Hupmobile car aged fourteen. His first competitive races were on motorcycles. Up until 1920 he had won 52 races and the following year he started to race in cars. He quickly distinguished himself with his courage, such as the time at the Tigullio circuit where his pneumatic tyres burst, but he still managed to reach the finish on the wheel rims. His legend is linked to epic battles in the Mille Miglia, the race which crossed Italy, where people would wait for hours to see the competitors zoom past. Nuvolari competed against the best racers of the age, ending his career in 1950 aged fifty-eight and worn out by the effects of a pulmonary disease. In 1970 Enzo Ferrari said of him, 'Men pass into history together with their moment in time, Nuvolari was an integral part of that period. The cruel modern world would certainly have attempted to harm him, but his skills were such that any poisonous attempts would have been strangled at birth.' Nuvolari died in his bed in Mantua on 11 August 1953. He was sixty-one years old.

Tazio Nuvolari and his Alfa Romeo in Nice, 1935

EMIL ZATOPEK

The son of a carpenter who was active in the underground communist movement, Emil Zatopek was born on 19 September 1922 at Koprivnice in Moravia. He came to running almost by accident as a student-worker at the Bata factory. From the start he specialised in middle and long distance races with a tenacity and dedication which became legendary and earned him the nickname of 'the human locomotive'. Not a great stylist, with heavy steps and face contorted in anguished exhaustion, Zatopek researched and put into practice an intensive training programme based on physical stamina. He holds a record which is unlikely ever to be beaten, where at the Helsinki Olympics of 1952 in the space of one week he won the 5,000 metres, 10,000 metres and marathon. After he stopped competing he was promoted to the rank of colonel in the Czechoslovakian army. As a result of his links with Dubcek he was demoted and dismissed from his post. He survived by working as a builder and later as a miner. He died aged seventy-eight on the night of 21 November 2000 following complications from a broken leg combined with a lung infection.

Emil Zatopek wins the marathon at the Helsinki Summer Olympic Games, July 1952

JEAN-ANTOINE CARREL AND EDWARD WHYMPER

Jean-Antoine Carrel was born in the village of Avouil, a part of Val Tournanche, in 1829. He fought in the War of Independence (1848–59) with the rank of sergeant, after which he was known as 'il Bersagliere'. A man with a strong temperament and a natural leader, his proud character was a determining factor in his challenge on the summit of the Matterhorn where he made his first attempt in 1857. Whymper's arrival on the scene and his attempt with a guide from Berne started the competition for the conquest of the mountain. His first attempt went as far as the Crete du Coq. Then in 1862, together with John Tyndall, he reached the point that from then on was known as the Enjambee del Pic Tyndall. Whymper's final defeat in 1865 and the leaving of Carrel's party in circumstances which remain murky, is a moment of alpine history around which a legend has grown. Above all this is because three days after his adversaries' tragic end, Carrel was able to conquer the Matterhorn climbing from the Italian side, which was more technically difficult than the route taken by the Englishman. In later years,

largely owing to mutual respect, their relationship improved and they undertook an expedition to the Andes, climbing several peaks together. Hunter, shepherd, artisan and farmer, Carrel climbed several other peaks apart from the Matterhorn until his fifty-first ascent where he died after saving his companions in his party at a place today remembered as 'Carrel's Cross'. It was 1890 and il Bersagliere was sixty-one years old.

Jean-Antoine Carrel,
woodcut, c.1850

Edward Whymper was born in London in 1840 from a family of Dutch origins. His father was a painter who passed on to him a talent which was to play a part in the development of his alpine activities. His interest in climbing began as a twenty-year-old when a publisher commissioned him to undertake a series of illustrations of alpine peaks, giving him his first contact with the mountains. The best climbers of the day such as Kennedy, Lesley Stephen, Walker, made a strong impression on him. So in 1861 Whymper felt pushed to go to Val Tournanche, where as Carrel knew, he would start a series of attempts which in 1865 took him to the top of the Matterhorn. The tragic events during the descent had a powerful impact on public opinion. For a long time people not only spoke of someone who set himself to climb a mountain, but of someone who became embroiled in bitter controversy that called into question his ability to be in charge of a climbing party as well as his own integrity. This raised infinite doubts about him which have never been completely resolved. As a result of the controversy he decided to cease

attempts on the biggest challenges, making an exception with his involvement in the South American expedition alongside his great rival Carrel. He died aged seventy-one, in retirement at Chamonix.

Edward Whymper in climbing gear, January 1865

FC START OF KIEV

Start of Kiev was a special team made up of players from Kiev's two main clubs during the Nazi occupation of 1942. Goncharenko, Sviridovskij, Korotkikh, Klimenko, Tyutchev, Putistin and Kuzmenko from the Dynamo team; Balakin, Sukharev and Melnik from Locomotive. With the passage of time their story has taken on legendary status, becoming known as "the death match", a legend that has historical foundations. Some players were killed, others died after deportation to concentration camps. For a long time the only survivor was Makar Goncharenko, standard-bearer and witness to that incredible team. Free interpretations of their story have inspired writers and film directors, such as the Hungarian Zoltan Fabri in *Twice in Hell* and John Huston with *Escape to Victory*. Still today those who own tickets from that terrible match hold the right to a place in the stand at Dynamo Kiev's stadium, which stands opposite a marble memorial to the deceased footballers.

The memorial outside Dynamo Kiev's stadium, in remembrance of
FC Start, the wartime football team

PIER PAOLO PASOLINI

Pasolini was born in Bologna on 5 March 1922. His father was an official in an artillery factory, his mother a primary school teacher, originally from the Friuli region that Pasolini was fond of since childhood holidays spent at Casarsa. He was a writer, poet and film director, and his intellectual drive was in continual conflict with the world he found around him. He centred his own life on an unceasing desire to redefine culture, politics, society and history. Using different forms to express his ideas, he searched for a way of expressing absolute truths and values capable of giving sense and power to various aspects of human existence. He was not afraid of living openly as a homosexual, a stark reality for the time, leaving himself open to disapproval and condemnation. He found continual conflict between the routine life and the intellectual life, vehemently denouncing the huge transformations that were happening across the fabric of Italian society, in a period of change between the agrarian and consumer models. He became absorbed and participated in diverse aspects of life, including areas which could seem insignificant, such as football, which he loved for its physical expression, and because of its potential as a kind of language. In one of his works he wrote: 'Football is a system of signs, so it is a language. It has all the characteristics of a language par excellence, the written/spoken language in fact. Those making the ciphers are the players; we in the stands

are the decipherers; so we are both in possession of a common code. Those who do not understand football's codes, do not understand the "significance" of its words (the passages) neither its sense or its discourse (the togetherness of its passages).' A fan of Bologna, Pasolini loved to play in improvised matches with his friends, where he played seriously and with passion, a passion which remained until his assassination on the dusty Idroscalo field at Ostia, on the night between 1 and 2 November 1975.

Pier Paolo Pasolini, September 1971